Kundalini Yoga

for Youth & Joy

Yogi Bhajan, Ph.D.
Master of Kundalini Yoga

Acknowledgements

The teachings in this manual are the gift of Yogi Bhajan, who brought the technology of Kundalini Yoga to the West. Our gratitude to him is infinite. Any errors or omissions in the following pages are entirely the fault of the Editors and by no means reflect upon the perfection and comprehensiveness of these teachings. We also wish to thank the women of Khalsa Women's Training Camp, Summer 1983, who helped in the preparation of this manuscript.

KRI 2nd Edition 2006
Library of Congress
ISBN 978-0-9720110-6-8

Consulting Editor
Dr. Sat Kirpal Kaur Khalsa

Copy Editors
Nam Kaur Khalsa
Dharma Kaur Khalsa
Satya Kaur Khalsa

Production Manager
Sat Mander Kaur Khalsa

Layout
Ravi Tej Singh Khalsa

Cover Design
Harbhajan Singh Khalsa

Cover Photograph
Gurudarshan Kaur Khalsa

Model On Cover
Hari Bhajan Kaur Khalsa
Illustrations
Hari Kaur Khalsa
Ravi Tej Kaur Khalsa

Typesetting
Pan Typesetters

Table of Contents

Introduction

This Yoga manual is the result of a six-week Kundalini Yoga course taught by Yogi Bhajan at Khalsa Women's Training Camp in Espanola, New Mexico, in the summer of 1983. Though originally taught to women, these exercises are intended for men as well. Yogi Bhajan is a Master of the ancient science of Kundalini Yoga. This manual gives a practical, step by step approach on how to develop a youthful body, an alert mind and a vibrant projection.

The exercises will leave you feeling healthy and energetic, with renewed enthusiasm for life. A body which is strong, flexible and radiant need not be young in years, as a stiff, slow, fragile body need not be advanced in age. An aging body is a body out of tune, out of shape and most often is the result of the inability to handle mental and physical stresses in the environment. Each system of the body-muscular, nervous, glandular, digestive, circulatory-is built up, stimulated and balanced so that you can experience your power and the flow of your energy as a complete human being.

As Yogi Bhajan explained:

There is no virtue in letting your body get stiff. When we leave the muscles unused for a long time, they start deteriorating and create a pressure on the living muscle cells. That is how we start getting older and weaker. The worst of it all is that our capacity to think and react and act to balance out our intuitive psyche also gets weaker and weaker. The whole of the physical system, the physiology, the muscles and the rhythm of the body have to be understood to keep all parts in balance. Towards that goal, I am going to work hard with you this summer. This is a very old and sophisticated system. It creates results which will be everlasting. You will build up your body and your muscles, and you will be very limber and very, very flexible. Gradually, one by one, we will work on all the main organs in the body: the glands, the circulation, the nerves, the muscles and the body constitution, and you will be surprised at the feelings and the changes which you have not experienced before.

About Yogi Bhajan

Yogi Bhajan, Master of Kundalini Yoga and Mahan Tantric of White Tantric Yoga, started teaching in America in January 1969. He was Director of Spiritual Education for the Healthy, Happy, Holy Organization (3H0), and the Kundalini Research Institute (KRI), until his passing on October 6, 2004.

In 1971, he inaugurated a new concept of teaching for women which has been the catalyst for dynamic change in the lives of thousands of women. Out of this developed Khalsa Women's Training Camp.

Yogi Bhajan traveled constantly, lecturing and teaching White Tantric Yoga, Kundalini Yoga and Meditation courses. Despite the amazing popularity of the spiritual way of life he has inspired in a basically materialistic era, Yogi Bhajan was a humble and pure channel of the Infinite. In his own words:

> *Somebody just shared his knowledge with me and by the Grace of God, I collected it. We are in a desert, and I have a little water with me that I want to share with people. Does that make me a water man? Am I the rain? Am I the clouds? Am I the ocean? No. I am just a little can of water in the desert to which people can touch their lips and think of surviving. Beyond that, I am nothing.*

Seventy-five publications bear Yogi Bhajan's name including: *The Teachings of Yogi Bhajan, The Aquarian Teacher, The Mind, The Master's Touch, Human Caliber, Contrast Consciousness, Mysteries of the Unknown*, several volumes of *Women in Training* and *Man to Man* and several Kundalini Yoga and Meditation manuals.

To find a Kundalini Yoga Instructor, visit the website of the International Kundalini Yoga Teachers Association (IKYTA) at www.kundaliniyoga.com, call 505-367-1313, or email IKYTA@3HO.org.

How to Begin

All exercise sets in Kundalini Yoga are complete in themselves in their effects on the body and mind. You may begin with slower speeds and shorter times and gradually work up to the speed and times given. Most of these sets were taught with no relaxation between the exercises; a relaxation at the end will help consolidate the effects of the whole set.

Ong Namo Guru Dev Namo: Adi Mantra

Chant this mantra at least three times before every class or practice of Kundalini Yoga or meditation. Sit in Easy Pose with the hands in Prayer Pose, thumbs pressing in slightly above the sternum. Close your eyes and focus at the third eye point. Vibrate the word *Ong* powerfully through the nose. Beginners may take a quick half breath after the first *Namo*.

This mantra opens the protective channel of energy for Kundalini Yoga. *Ong* is the infinite creative energy; *Namo* means "I bow"; *Guru* means teacher who brings you from darkness to light; *Dev* is the Etheric Divinity of God. The meaning of the mantra is:

"I bow to the Infinite Creative Consciousness. I bow to the Divine Wisdom within and without."

Basic Mudras

Gyan Mudra:

To form Gyan Mudra put the tips of the thumb and index finger together. This stimulates knowledge, receptivity and calmness. The energy of the index finger is symbolized by Jupiter, the planet representing expansion. In the practice of powerful pranayam or exercises, the "active" form of Gyan Mudra may be indicated; bend the index finger under the thumb so the fingernail is on the thumb's second joint.

Venus Lock:

This mudra connects the positive and negative sides of the Venus mound (the fleshy area at the base of the thumbs) to the thumbs. Which represent the ego. The Venus mound is symbolized by the planet Venus which is associated with the energy of sensuality and sexuality. The mudra channels the sexual energy and promotes glandular balance. Relaxing the hands in your lap in this mudra enables you to concentrate easily in meditation.

To form the mudra men should interlace the fingers with the left little finger on the bottom, and put the left thumb tip just above the base of the right thumb on the webbing between the thumb and index finger. The tip of the right thumb presses the fleshy mound at the base of the left thumb. Women have the right pinky on the bottom and reverse the thumbs.

Prayer Pose:

For this mudra, the palms of the hands are flat together. The positive side of the body (right, or male) and negative (left, or female) are neutralized.

Basic Sitting Postures

Easy Pose:

Sit Indian style in cross legged position with your spine straight and your lower spine slightly forward.

Rock Pose (Vajrasana)

This asana is well known for its beneficial effects on the digestive system. It gained its nickname from the idea that one who masters this posture can sit in it and "digest rocks." It also makes you solid and balanced as a rock.

Kneel on both knees with the top of the feet on the ground, then sit back on the heels. The heels will press the two nerves that run into the lower center of each buttock. Keep the spine straight.75

Breath of Fire

This breath is used consistently throughout Kundalini Yoga kriyas. It is very important that Breath of Fire be mastered by the student. In Breath of Fire, the focus of energy is at the navel point. The breath is fairly rapid (2 to 3 breaths per second), continuous and powerful with no pause between the inhale and exhale. As you exhale, the air is pushed out by pulling the navel point and abdomen towards the spine. In this motion, the chest area is moderately relaxed. As you inhale, use the forward thrust of the navel point to bring the air into the lungs. This is a very balanced breath with no emphasis on either the exhale or the inhale, and with equal power given to both. Breath of Fire cleans the blood and releases old toxins from the lungs, mucous lining, blood vessels and cells. Regular practice expands the lungs quickly.

Long Deep Breathing

The simplest of all the yogic breaths is long deep breathing; a habit that we as a culture do not have. Our normal tendency is to breathe shallowly, which leads to an emotional approach to life, chronic tension and weak nerves. Besides supplying oxygen to and removing carbon dioxide from the body, the respiratory system helps regulate body pH (acidity-alkalinity) and helps excrete water vapor, hydrogen and small amounts of methane. The average lungs can enlarge to a volume of almost 6,000 cubic centimeters. Normally we use only 600 or 700 cubic centimeters. If you do not expand the lungs to full capacity, the small air sacs in the lungs cannot clean their mucous lining properly, and toxic irritants build up.

To take a full yogic breath, inhale by first relaxing the abdomen. Next expand the chest. As you exhale let the chest deflate first, then pull the belly in completely. The diaphragm drops down to expand the lungs and contracts up to expel the air.

By taking a deep yogic breath you can expand the lungs by about eight times. If you establish a habit of breathing deeply and slowly you will have endurance and patience. If you can take the breath down below eight times per minute the pituitary starts secreting fully. If the breath is less than four times per minute the pineal gland starts functioning fully and deep meditation is automatic.

Mental Focus & Music

Generally speaking, unless you are instructed to do otherwise, you should fix your concentration at the third-eye point, a point midway between the brows, one-half inch up and one-half inch below the skin. With your eyes closed, you can mentally locate this point by turning your eyes gently upwards and inwards. Remain aware of your breath, your body posture, your movements and any mantra you may be using, and allow your "center of awareness" to be at the third-eye point.

Yogi Bhajan explained that only Kundalini Yoga music should be used in Kundalini Yoga classes:

Kundalini Yoga is to create inner energy, not to provoke outer energy. Music must be within a certain rhythm. Music that is more physical or mental than spiritual can stop rhythm. Ours should be more spiritual. Commitment to self is not a joke. Commotional music is not required. If the music is not soothing, if it creates commotion, it is not allowed. A yoga class needs elevation, projection of the proper combination and permutation of words which push you through. You need a rocket for taking this space shuttle, right? Now what are you going to do? Use a few fans and think it is going up? That's wrong. Kundalini Yoga is not a pop festival, nor is it a rock and roll concert. It has those subtle projections through which the person can go inward. When you are teaching, be with the purity of the essence as you have been taught.

Ishnaan, the Science of Hydrotherapy

I'd like to share the technology and science of a type of massage with you. It is called hydrotherapeutic massage. As I'm sitting before you, my first qualification and field of expertise is in hydrotherapy. You may not have known that, and there is no one else with this qualification in the whole world. I carry the lineage of those who now are very unknown, but who once were worshipped. They worked on the bones, adjusted the body and did massage to recreate healthy organs.

Since ancient times, people have prayed for the blessing of Ishnaan. What is Ishnaan? Ishnaan is the total sum of hydrotherapy. The word is Ishnaan. We don't say we'll take a bath; we never say "bath." Ishnaan is when the body, by its own virtue, creates the temperature that it can beat off the coldness of the water. Ishnaan is not just wetting your body. There is a whole respect to it. There is a whole grace to it.

The power of water is sixty percent of the power of the human. In hydrotherapy we believe that the sixty percent water in the body can be totally exchanged in sixty minutes with outside water. We do ice cold water massage and not only do we open up the capillaries, but then when they close down again, that is, return to normal, that blood goes back to the organs. The heart, kidneys, lungs, liver-each organ has its own blood supply. In this way the organs get their flushing. When the organs get a flushing, then immediately the glands have to change their secretion. It is a law. And when the glands change, the guardians of the health and life change, youth returns. What is youth? Young glands. Young glands are called youth. If your glandular system secretes correctly, the blood chemistry is a young chemistry, and the glands can be made to do it. All this neurotic neurosis and angriness will all be over.

This science of hydrotherapy is very precise and sophisticated, and very simple. If you take a cold shower and let it fall just below the lower lip for ten or fifteen minutes, you will be bright and your mind will be very clear. If you put the water between the eyebrows and the upper lip, you will be very energetic. And if you put the water on the forehead, you will be so sleepy that you can't match it. If you massage the upper arm under a very cold shower from your elbow to just below your shoulder on your upper arm, you are totally curing your stomach. From your elbow to about two inches above your wrist corresponds to your digestive tract. Two inches above the wrist to the start of the wrist corresponds to your heart. The wrist corresponds to your liver and the finger tips correspond to your brain.

Then if you put the water on your neck in the front and let the water run down your entire body and hands, you will totally change all your cells. And if you let the water hit your chest and go all the way down to your genitals and you stay under it for a while, you are totally changing the chemistry of the blood from unhealthy to healthy. If you let the water hit your feet and massage the right foot with the left foot, and the left foot with the right foot, you are actually massaging your entire body. Stand before a cold shower and massage your feet and your calves by yourself. Use your feet to massage, don't use your hands. Then stand away from the water and using both hands, massage your entire body and let the body get hot. Then take a cold shower again and massage your body again. Do that for about twelve to fifteen minutes. You should have a friend handy to pull you out. You will be in a totally different space.

Your body will be totally rebuilt. Each organ will be rebuilt. How? When you take a cold shower, your blood rushes out to meet the challenge. This means all the capillaries open up and all deposits have to go. Everything is cleaned; it is a very cleansing process. During hydrotherapy, the body is challenged by the cold water and by massaging the body, it can meet this challenge and not feel cold.

Do you understand this? When you are under the cold shower, your body will feel the cold, right? But when the blood and the capillaries are totally opened up to the maximum, the body will not feel cold. I repeat, it will not feel cold. And if you bring your body to that temperature where it can meet the cold by its own circulatory power, then all you have to do is come out and totally towel yourself, put on warm clothes, and put a blanket around you. Or if it is hot weather like it is here, use a big bath towel.

Bath towels are for the hydrotherapists, not for you. It's not a fashion. You don't even know how to use them. They are like blankets. Roll yourself up in one. Then your body will become wild hot. All the blood that is in the capillaries and in circulation will go back to the organs: the kidneys, the liver, the spleen, the lungs-because each part of your body lives on its own blood supply which is regulated by the beat of the heart. So the organs will get a rich supply of blood like a crop getting a beautiful rain, and then the crop grows up. In exactly the same way, this is how you can balance your health.

They didn't know how to make a shower when they first did hydrotherapy. You are very lucky you have modern showers. In ancient times there was nothing. They had to fill a tub that was about thirty to forty feet above the ground. It was huge and men had to fill it with water. It required about five hundred men to create enough water pressure for the hydrotherapy. When the machine age came they used a booster pump to create that effect. Have you ever taken a bath under a booster shower? It's fun. They take a pump that has a booster which comes through the shower head. It is so powerful, so wonderful; it's marvelous. We used to have a handle and a pipe and the pipe was flexible. For somebody who lay down under it, it had a tremendously soothing effect.

Now we have showers in every house, but the art of hydrotherapy is lost. Now a little pill can help you, and you can be on your own again. That is fine, but the difference between people today and people then is that today people want to be healthy, but they are not afraid of being sick. In those days, people were afraid of being sick; they never wanted to be unhealthy. That is how times have changed for us; that's what we are. Allopathic medicine is very effective. The chemical goes right in, right to the spot and it takes care of you. But the unfortunate part of it is that it has its side effects.

Body cells recuperate themselves in seventy-two hours. Sometimes they get delayed. Recuperation becomes slower as you become older; it's the time phase. But in hydrotherapy we believe youth is permanent, and youth is permanent not because it's God's gift. Youth is permanent because we know how to be young. It's a challenge but people who have done hydrotherapy have seen that they have remained young by their own virtue. I myself have seen my teacher, Sant Hazara Singh, remain ageless, so long as he did it.

By doing any exercise for hours, you cannot stimulate your cell psyche to the extent that you can with cold water. And the procedure is very simple. Take your hands, let the cold water fall, and rub them to the extent that they become hot under the ice cold water. And so with every part of the body; let it go, let it be, and stimulate yourself. And this stimulation may look to you like a fanatic, painful attitude, but that's what it is all about. Some people do deep muscle massage, some people go to spas, and others do this or that. There are one million methods and nothing even comes close to this one. There's nothing like standing under ice cold water and making your body become hot. The word is "hot." Normally, in this therapy, we say to "heat yourself,"-heat your neck, heat your shoulders, heat your elbows. Can you believe a guy standing under a shower doing this for two hours? But that's how they do it. And everywhere that the cold water hits, the blood will come. Everywhere you massage, rebuilding will occur and the psyche of each cell of the body will be reconstructed.

Sometimes in your own life, you do not value your life. And then you cannot value it, because you are old. So play no such games with yourself; death will come, don't bother. Richness will come, don't bother. Poverty will come, no bother. Disease will come, no bother. Bother for nothing. But if you have a strong-built mind, body and soul, everything will come. All adversity will come, but it won't touch you, because nobody wants to pick a fight with a powerful man. Therefore, the saying in hydrotherapy is, "shield yourself." In hydrotherapy, they think that water is a fatherly shield, paanee pitaa, and that anybody who can produce this shield that conquers the coldness of the water can conquer death. That's what hydrotherapy is based on. It's a very simple thing. If I with my body can conquer the chilliness of the water, I can take away the chilliness of my life.

Kriya for the Sciatic Nerve

1) Stand up. Stretch the left arm straight out to the side. Raise the right leg straight out to the side, as high as possible, and lower it. Continue moving the leg up and down once every 1-2 seconds. Do not change sides. The arm is held stationary. Continue for 2 minutes.
This exercise works on balancing the brain and stretching the sciatic nerve.

2) Stand with the feet 18 inches apart. Extend both arms up to exactly 60°, elbows straight. Twist the whole body from left to right. Move fast. Continue powerfully for 5 minutes.
This exercise works on the liver. The 60° angle of the arms allows for the stimulation in this area to occur.

3) Stand with the arms extended up at 60°, palms flat facing forward, fingers spread and taut. Alternate the arms crossing in front of the face and returning them to the original position. Move as fast as you can; make yourself sweat. The eyes remain open throughout the exercise. Continue powerfully for 4 minutes.
This exercise stimulates the meridian points in the arm.

4) Stand up. Raise the arms straight over the head with the fingers interlaced into Venus Lock. Inhale and bend backward, and then exhale and stretch forward. One complete cycle takes 2-3 seconds. Concentrate on involving your whole body. Continue for 4 minutes.
This exercise works on the rib cage.

5) Stand with the arms extended directly out to the sides, elbows straight, palms down. Begin to rapidly move the arms up and down within a 15° arc, in a flapping motion. Your breath will regulate itself with the exercise and become very deep and powerful. Continue rhythmically, coordinating the movement with the breath for 2 minutes.
This exercise is stimulating and prepares you for the heavy exercises to follow:

6) Stand with your feet 24 inches apart. Put your hands on your thighs just above the knees. Arch the lower back in Cow Pose. Move the buttocks up and down, leaning on the hands. The knees will flex. One complete cycle takes 1-2 seconds. 2 minutes.
This exercise slowly adjusts the 3rd, 4th, 5th and 6th lumbar vertebrae.

7) Sit down with both the legs and arms extended straight out in front, parallel to the ground. Inhale, exhale and stretch forward keeping the lower back arched back as in Cat Pose, arms parallel to the ground. One cycle takes 2-3 seconds. Continue for 2 minutes. *This exercise applies pressure to the lower back.*

8) Remain sitting with the legs straight out. Lock both hands under the left knee and rapidly begin to raise the leg all the way up and all the way down, keeping it straight. One complete cycle takes 2 seconds. Continue powerfully for 1-2 minutes. Then repeat the exercise on the opposite side for 1-2 minutes. *This exercise works on the colon and liver.*

9) Sitting with the legs extended, lean back resting on your hands; elbows slightly bent. Raise both legs 18 inches and begin an alternate push-pull motion, keeping the line of motion parallel to the ground. Move quickly and powerfully for 3 minutes. *This exercise stimulates and adjusts the hips. It is recommended especially for women to do before they get out of bed in the morning. It has been said that this exercise keeps one youthful.*

10) Sit in Easy Pose. Inhale and extend the arms straight up making the hands into fists. Exhale and bring them down to the sides at shoulder height with the fingers opened. Continue for 2 minutes. *This exercise works on circulation.*

11) Come into Frog Pose, a squatting position with the heels off the ground and touching each other, and the fingertips placed on the floor in front of you. Roll your head completely around on your shoulders, letting the chin touch the chest. Continue for 1 minute. *This exercise works on the spine and the lower back.*

12) Remain in Frog Pose. Start with the fingertips placed on the floor in front of you. Alternately raise the elbows all the way up making the hands into fists, and then lower them back down. One complete cycle takes 2-3 seconds. Continue for 2-3 minutes. *This exercise works on the shoulder area.*

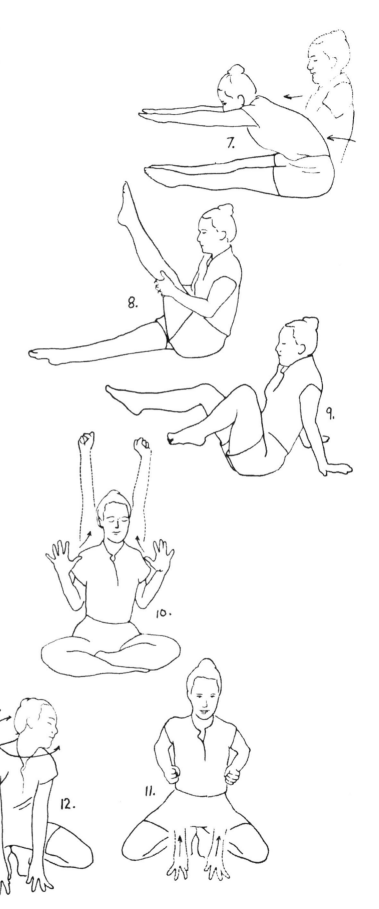

13) Shushmana (Corpse Pose). Lie on your back with your arms at your sides, palms up, ankles uncrossed and eyes closed. Let the body go dead. Completely relax the body systematically part by part, beginning with the feet and continuing on up to the head. Make the breath long and deep. Concentrate at the third eye point. Feel young and beautiful. Continue to deeply relax for 5 minutes.

14) Remain on the back and bend your knees, keeping your feet on the floor, heels together. Bring the knees together, and then spread them apart towards the floor, with the heels still touching. Move as fast as you can. Continue this flapping motion for 2 minutes.
This exercise adjusts the hips.

15) Lying on your back, hug your knees and draw them to your chest. Slowly bring your nose up to your knees, and then lower it back down (4 seconds up, 4 seconds down). Continue for 3 minutes.
This exercise stimulates the thyroid.

16) Sit in Easy Pose. Place the right palm over the left hand in front of your chest, both palms facing down. Your arms are parallel to the ground and the spine is straight. Look at the tip of the nose and with the tip of the tongue chant *Har, Har, Har* continuously (8 repetitions of *Har* every 4 seconds). Continue rhythmically for 2 minutes. Then begin to draw the navel point in towards the spine each time the tip of the tongue touches the upper palate on Har. Continue for 2 more minutes.

17) Remain in Easy Pose, same position as number 16. Inhale, hold the breath and puff out the cheeks as fully as you can. Breath through your nose and keep the cheeks puffed out, releasing a little more air into your mouth after each inhale. Increase the pressure. Continue for 1-2 minutes. Then with your cheeks still puffed out and the head stationary, begin to move your eyes left, right, up and down, continuing the breath for 1 minute more.
This exercise increases circulation to the eyes and cheeks. It is good for the complexion because it flushes all the cells in the face. It rejuvenates those cells which typically get very little blood circulation.

18) Sit in Easy Pose. Press your palm against the side of your head and resist with your neck muscles. Apply maximum pressure. Alternately press to the right and left side (2 seconds to each side). Continue for 2-3 minutes.
This exercise will keep your neck in proper alignment.

19) Relax. Sing any song of your choice and relax into it.

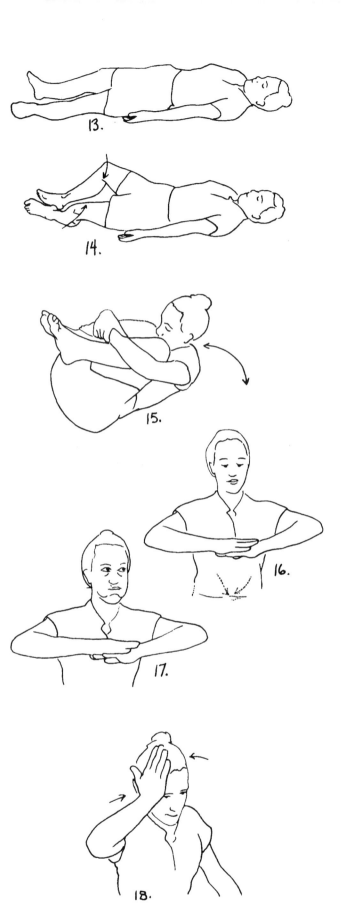

Kriya for Electromagnetic Frequency

1) Sit in Easy Pose. Extend the arms out to the sides with the fingers stretched and tensed like claws. The entire hand should be rigid and taut like a lion's paw. Alternately cross your wrists overhead and return the arms out to the side, parallel to the ground. Keep the lion's paw tight. Move powerfully and rhythmically. Begin breath of fire, coordinating one inhale-exhale with each movement for 9 minutes, then without stopping, stick your tongue all the way out and continue for 15 seconds.

Inhale and hold the arms up at 60 degrees for 15 seconds. Exhale. Repeat. Inhale and hold again for 30 seconds. Exhale and relax by singing the song "Nobility" from the heart for 3-4 minutes or sit quietly breathing long and gently.

This exercise works on the electromagnetic frequency of the brain. The hand position pressurizes all the fingertips which control the brain and its functions. The lymph and nervous systems are tuned up and the powerful breath of fire stimulates the pituitary gland and causes the pineal gland to change the frequency of the radiance of your magnetic field..

Kriya for the Liver, Colon and Stomach

1) Stand with your legs 2 feet apart. Place your hands on your hips. Bend from the waist to the right, to the left, then forward and back, returning to the upright position after each bend. One second in each direction. Chant aloud, *Sa* as you bend to the right, *Ta* to the left, *Na* to the front and *Ma* to the back. Continue rhythmically, coordinating the movement with the mantra for 5 minutes.

This exercise opens up the hip area and prepares you for the next exercise.

2) Remain in a standing position with your legs 2 feet apart and the hands on the hips. Begin to roll the upper torso around on your hips. Roll to your maximum capacity, bending completely in all directions. Continue for 2-3 minutes, one second per roll. Then start chanting *Har Hari,* once with each roll for 2 minutes more.

This exercise stimulates the gonads.

3) Stand with your legs apart and your arms relaxed down at your sides. Bring the arms up, parallel to the ground and cross them grasping the upper arms. Lean back and let your arms come up and back, pulling your breast muscle up. Return to starting position and then relax your arms down at your sides. Chant aloud *Sa-Ta-Na-Ma* rhythmically coordinating the movement with the mantra for 3-4 minutes.

This exercise relieves lower back pain and pressurizes the lymph area.

4) Remain standing with the arms parallel to the ground grasping the upper arms. Do deep knee bends squatting into Crow Pose, with the feet flat on the floor. As you go up and down chant aloud *Sa-Ta-Na-Ma*. Coordinate the movement with the mantra powerfully and rhythmically as follow: *Sa* -down, *Ta* -up, *Na* -down, *Ma* - up. Continue for 3 minutes.
This exercise balances the body's energy. It also works to relieve pain in the lower back.

5) Continue standing with the legs apart. Put your thumbs on the Mercury mounds (the mound below the little finger, palm side) and make your hands into fists. Swing your arms backwards in large rapid circles, making sure to move the shoulders. Chant aloud *Har Har Har Har Har Har Hari*, 2-3 circles per repetition. Continue rhythmically coordinating the movement with the mantra for 2-3 minutes.
This exercise balances the psyche and enhances communication skills.

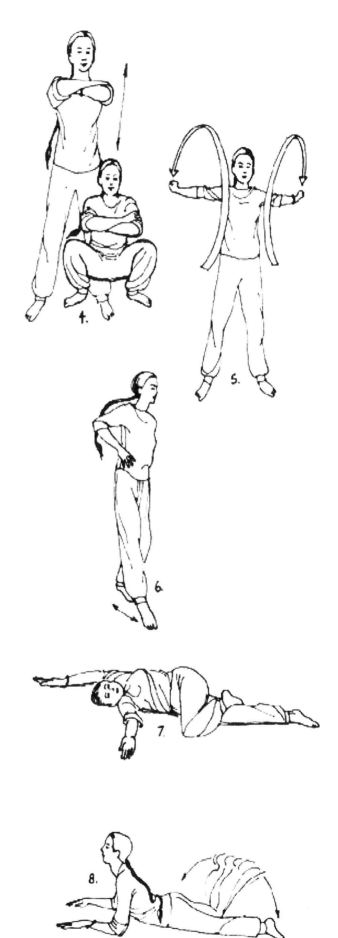

6) Stand on the balls of your feet and place your hands on your hips. Kick your feet forward alternately in a jogging, shuffling motion. Use a fast pace. Chant aloud, *Hum Dum Har Har, Har Har Hum Dum*. Continue rhythmically, coordinating the movement with the mantra for 3 minutes.
This exercise balances the metals in the body.

7) Immediately lie down with your legs straight and begin a Cat Stretch to both sides, alternately bending the knees and touching them to the ground on the other side of the straight leg. Continue this powerfully for 1-2 minutes.
This exercise puts a pressure on the liver and removes toxins. It also consolidates the effects of the previous exercises.

8) Come into Half Cobra Pose. Lie on the stomach with your neck up and chin out, palms flat on the floor under the shoulders. Keep the heels together with the soles of the feet facing up. Inhale and arch the spine up while resting on the forearms. Begin to kick your buttocks hard with alternate heels. Continue for 3-4 minutes at a moderate pace. Switch to a rapid pace for the last minute. Total exercise time should be 4-5 minutes.
This exercise is specifically for regulating the calcium/ magnesium balance in the blood stream and body which is controlled by the thighbone. This bone also controls one's sexuality. The exercise also applies a maximum pressure to the parathyroid and thyroid when the neck is up and the chin is out.

9) Squat in Frog Pose so the buttocks touch your heels and the heels are off the ground touching each other. Put the fingertips on the ground between the knees and keep the head up. Inhale, raise the buttocks high, keeping the fingers on the ground. Exhale, come down and let the buttocks strike the heels. The exhale should be strong. Chant aloud *Sa-Ta-Na-Ma* rhythmically coordinating the movement with the mantra for 2 minutes.
This exercise works on the knees.

10) Stand up straight with the arms down by your sides. Then sit down in a cross-legged position. Alternate this
This exercise balances the prana and apana in the body.

11) Repeat exercise 9 for 30 seconds.

12) Lie down on your back. Keeping the legs straight, lift them up and grab on to your toes with your hands. Exhale through the nose. Continue for 1-2 minutes.
The breath used in this exercise cools the body off.

13) Sit in Easy Pose. Place the arms at shoulder level with the finger tips meeting at the center of the chest, palms facing out Alternating left to right, straighten the arms out to the side with a jerk to the elbow and return to the center. Continue for 3 minutes.
This exercise works directly on the forearm muscle which regulates the colon.

15.

14) Sit in Easy Pose. Place the hands on the knees. Focusing on the upper spine and shoulders, inhale and flex the spine forward. As you exhale, flex the spine back, keeping the shoulders relaxed and the head straight. Continue at a moderate pace for 4 minutes.

This exercise is for the lymph area and is reported by some people to prevent breast cancer. If done correctly it will create an unusual pressure behind the ears on the neck. It means your whole nervous system and central nervous system, the Sushmana, is stretching. It should create a sweat on the face.

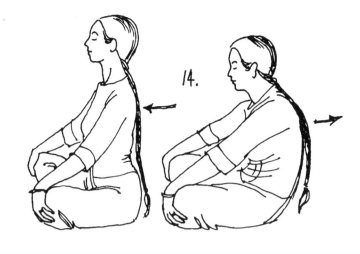

15) Remain sitting in Easy Pose. Make loose fists of the hands by placing the thumbs on the inside and wrapping the fingers loosely around the thumbs. In a rapid movement, inhale and extend the arms up. Exhale and lower the arms with the fists returning to shoulder level. Continue for 2-3 minutes.

This exercise works on the spine and the sciatic nerve.

16) Sit in Easy Pose. Cross your arms at the heart center, grasping the upper arms. Chant aloud *Sa-Ta-Na-Ma* as you begin to bend your head in the following manner: Right, center, left, center. Complete one cycle every 2-3 seconds. Continue rhythmically coordinating the movement with the mantra for 1-2 minutes.

This exercise adjusts the neck.

17) Sing the song '*Nobility*'' for 4 minutes or sit meditatively and breathe long and gently for 4 minutes.

Kriya for the Lymph System

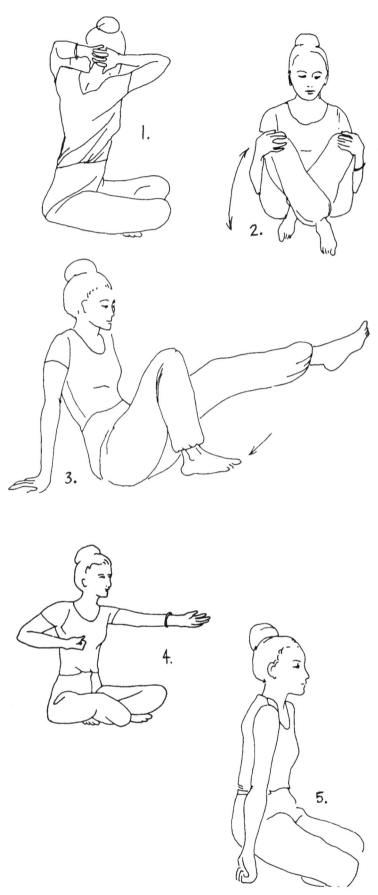

1) Sit in Easy Pose. Interlace the fingers into Venus Lock and place behind the head where the neck and scalp join. Extend the elbows straight out to the sides, parallel to the ground. Begin twisting powerfully from left to right, stopping for one count in the center (1 second in each direction). Inhale to each side, exhale in the center. Twist completely to each side. Continue for 9 minutes.

This exercise removes tension from the shoulders and relaxes the muscles of the breast. When the breast muscles are not relaxed, the stomach muscles are stressed which causes fat to deposit around the abdomen. When the shoulder muscles are stretched, the supply of blood to the brain is regulated.

2) Sitting in Easy Pose, grasp the outside of the knees. Keep the spine straight and with the power of the hands begin pulling the knees up towards each other in front of the chest and lowering them down (one cycle takes less than one second). Continue for 6 minutes.

The exercise applies a tremendous pressure to the breast and stomach area. It also works on breaking down the fat around the abdomen and adjusts the ankles and knees.

3) Stretch both legs straight out in front. Keeping your arms straight, lean back on your hands and point them backwards. Bend the knees up and rapidly and powerfully start kicking your legs up and down in the air. Keep ankles and feet relaxed and concentrate on moving from below the knees. Continue for 3 minutes.

This exercise works on the lower spine.

4) In Easy Pose, sit with a straight spine. Extend the arms straight in front of you at a slight angle outwards, parallel to the ground, with the palms facing up. Alternately, make fists of the hands and pull them into the shoulder area. Pull hard enough to make the body shake and move rapidly. Continue for 1-2 minutes.

This exercise works on opening up the arteries.

5) Sit in Easy Pose. Place the flat part of your fist on the floor next to your hips. Keeping the back straight and the heels on the floor, lift the body up and then drop it down (1-2 times every second). Continue for 4 minutes.

This exercise builds up the shoulder muscles so that the lower torso is able to relax. It gives the shoulders a workout they never get in day to day life.

17.

6) Remain sitting in Easy Pose. Place the hands on the knees. Begin bending left to right from the waist to each side, adding a little distance with each bend. One complete cycle takes 2-3 seconds. 5-6 minutes.
This exercise aids in digestion.

7) In Easy Pose, sit with a straight spine and place the hands on the knees. Bend your head forward, back, left, right, returning to the center after each bend. Silently chant *Sa* as you bend forward, *Ta* to the back, *Na* to the left and *Ma* to the right. Continue rhythmically, coordinating the movement with the mantra for 2-3
This exercise strengthens the neck.

8) Lion Lick: Sit in Easy Pose. Place the hands on the knees and begin flexing your spine forwards and backwards. When the spine is flexed back, draw the chin to the chest and stick the whole tongue out as you make the sound "*Hunh.*" Inhale through the nose as the spine is flexed forward, drawing the tongue back into the mouth. Continue rhythmically for 3 minutes. (One complete cycle takes approximately one second.)
This exercise works on opening up the lungs.

9) Stand up. Place the feet shoulder-width apart, with the toes facing slightly out. Placing the hands on the knees, begin squatting down and coming halfway up keeping the feet flat on the floor. The knees will act as a fulcrum, helping maintain the same angle between the back and thighs throughout the exercise. Continue rhythmically for a maximum of 8 minutes, resting when needed. (One complete cycle takes less than one second.)
This exercise works directly on the knees. If the knees lose their elasticity, it can affect the alignment of the whole body, subsequently causing less circulation of blood to the breast area and increasing the chance of tumors.

10) Sit down. Stretch both legs straight out in front and keep the spine erect, hands resting in the lap or on the thighs. Alternately point your toes forward, and then. flex your feet back (one complete cycle takes 1-2 seconds.) Continue for 1 minute.
This exercise strengthens the muscles of the lower leg.

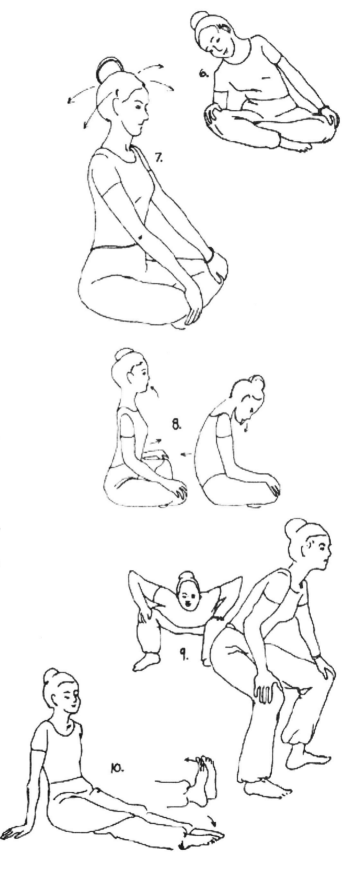

11) Sit in Easy Pose. Place the hands on the knees and begin rotating the abdominal area and lower spine around in large circles; roll only to the right. (One complete rotation takes 1-2 seconds.) Continue for 3-4 minutes.
This exercise works on digestion.

12) Remain sitting in Easy Pose with the hands on the knees. Rapidly begin shaking the head from left to right in short, sharp movements. Allow all the muscles of the mouth and face to relax. Continue for 3 minutes.
As you loosen up and shake, the pituitary gland, the temples and everything in the head area will move. It allows the capillaries to get their blood supply and strengthens all the muscles of the cheeks and jaw.

13) Sit in Easy Pose. Extend the arms out in front at chest level with slightly bent elbows. The palms are facing each other with the fingers spread apart. Rapidly shake the hands towards the center of the body and out, keeping the wrists loose. The motion is precisely in and out, not every which way. Shake so fast that you feel the fingers cutting the air and the hands feel separate from the body. Continue for 2-3 minutes.
This is an excellent exercise for the sciatic nerve. It stimulates circulation and removes the poisons.

14) Sit in Easy Pose. Place the hands in the lap. Begin chanting *Har, Har, Har, Har, Har, Har, Hari* continuously with the tip of the tongue (one complete repetition takes 2-3 seconds). Draw the navel point in each time the tip of the tongue touches the upper palate behind the teeth. Continue chanting rhythmically for 3-4 minutes.
This is a meditation for endurance.

15) In Easy Pose, stretch the arms over the head. Interlace the fingers of both hands with the palms facing up. Lean back and begin stretching from side to side like a cat. Continue for 1 minute.
This exercise balances the meridians in the rib cage and the area above it.

16) Sit in Easy Pose. Begin chanting: *God and Me, Me and God, Are One* for 3 minutes. Then chant: *I Am Thee, Thou Is Me, Me Is Thou* for 2-3 minutes. Finally chant: *All Things Come From God and All Things Go To God* for 2 minutes.

Kriya for the Lungs and Bloodstream

1) Sit in Easy Pose with a straight spine. Hold onto your knees with your hands. Inhale completely, stretching your ribcage to your maximum capacity. Do not sip more air in later, and don't leak. Place your tongue behind the teeth against the back of the upper teeth at the roof of the mouth. Relax the spine, keeping the breath held in. Begin flexing the spine rapidly until you can no longer hold the breath in and then exhale. Gradually increase the time you hold your breath to one minute. Continue for 11 minutes.

This exercise is an excellent way to build stamina, to make the blood suck up the oxygen from the lungs, and to help the heart muscles regulate and reorganize themselves. It will pressurize the kidneys, gonads and adrenals. It is necessary to be able to hold a full inhale for 1 minute in order to supply optimum oxygen to the blood stream. When less than the required oxygen is available in the blood, the brain, organs and glands are unable to function properly and the systems break down causing illness. When this exercise is done for 11 minutes a day or a maximum of 22 minutes, it will totally purify the bloodstream

It is suggested that if you do it for 22 minutes to take a rest after the first 11 minutes and then continue for 11 minutes more.

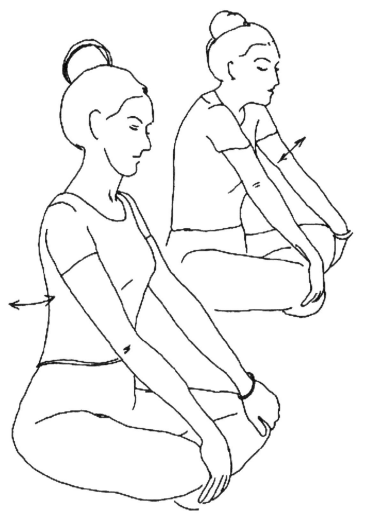

Kriya for the Kidneys

1) Sit with the legs and arms extended straight in front of you. Tightly fold the fingers onto the pads and point the thumbs up. In this position, inhale, exhale and bend all the way forward from the hips, keeping the arms parallel to the ground. Use a heavy, powerful breath. The breath must get heavier and heavier as you continue. Do 2 bends every 5 seconds for 5-6 minutes.

2) Lie down on your back, bend the knees and grasp the ankles. Inhale and raise the buttocks, pressing the navel point up; exhale down. The feet and neck remain on the ground. Move rhythmically for 8 minutes.
This exercise works on the neck, kidneys, urinary tract, and is helpful for hernia problems. The heavy breath stimulates the pituitary gland to secrete.

3) Come into a Cat/Cow position supporting yourself on your hands and knees. The knees are about shoulder width apart and the arms should be straight. Begin Cat/Cow with a heavy breath, inhaling as you flex your spine downwards as if someone were sitting on your back while your head arches up and back, exhaling as you flex the spine in the opposite direction. Continue for 2 minutes. Then remain in Cow Pose and stretch the left leg back and up. Hold for 30 seconds and switch to the right leg for 30 seconds. Now switch back to the left leg and kick the left buttock with the heel for 1 minute. Change and kick the right heel for 30 seconds.
This exercise works on the kidneys.

4) Lie on your back. Wrap your arms around your shins and hug the knees to the chest. Tuck your nose up between your knees and hold it there while you relax in this position for 1-2 minutes. Then maintain this posture and sing *"Nobility"* for 5-6 minutes followed by *"All Things Come from God"* for 2 minutes, or breathe long and gently for 7-9 minutes.

5) Sit in Crow Pose, a crouching position with the knees drawn into the chest and the soles of the feet flat on the ground. Stretch the arms straight out in front, parallel to the ground and balance yourself for 1 minute. Then begin continuously chanting *Har, Har, Har* with the tip of the tongue hitting the upper palate with each repetition. Feel the connection between the tip of the tongue and the navel. Chant for 2-3 minutes, then inhale deeply, tighten the lips and mouth and balance the entire body with the breath. Hold this breath 20 seconds, feeling that you are in total control, then exhale. Inhale and tighten again, balance your body under your control 30 seconds, then exhale and relax.
This exercise totally stimulates the kidneys and urinary tract. If you feel dizzy during the exercise, it is an indication that you need to drink more water.

6) Sit in Easy Pose with the hands are in Gyan Mudra. The left forearm is parallel to the ground in front of the chest, palm facing down. The right forearm is near the side, perpendicular to the ground, elbow bent sharply. The right palm faces up along side of the ear, stretching back as far as possible. Stretch your spine up. Pull up on the muscles of the buttocks, hips and sides lifting the upper body until there is very little weight on the buttocks. Pull in the abdomen and lift the ribs and diaphragm up, chest out, chin in. Hold 30 seconds, then let the tension go. Continue for 5 minutes, then inhale and relax.

Now maintain this strong upward pull, and with the tip of the tongue chant *Wahe Guru, Wahe Guru, Wahe Guru, Wahe Jeeo.* Keep the waists drawn up. The eyes will feel heavy and the breath will automatically become very light. Accuracy of the mudra is essential. Continue for 5 minutes then inhale and relax.
This exercise is called Kunchun Mudra. It is very powerful and purifying. It enables total relaxation of the body. When the posture is very accurate, it is equal to exercising 48 hours straight. There is no limit to the length of time you can practice this mudra but make sure to build your time slowly.

Kriya for Circulation

1) Sit in Crow Pose, flat on the floor. Keeping the spine straight, bend the arms so they are parallel to the ground at chest level, fingertips touching, palms down. The arm movements for this exercise are as follows: alternating arms, extend one arm straight out to the side, and then bring it back to the original position, then the other. Continuing the arm movements, begin rising to a standing position in 8 counts. By the count of 4 you should be half-way up. Use a powerful breath of fire and mentally chant *Sa-Ta-Na-Ma*, rhythmically coordinating the movements with the breath and mantra for 11 minutes.
This exercise works on the abdomen, pelvis and thighs and is very important for good health in a woman.

2) Sit in Easy Pose or Lotus Pose. Interlace the fingers in Venus Lock overhead, index fingers extended, and elbows straight. Inhale, stretch up. Exhale and stretch as you bring the forehead down to the left knee, keeping the buttocks on the ground. Inhale and return to the starting position. Exhale and stretch down to the right knee. Continue at a moderate pace alternating from left to right for 3 minutes.
This exercise works on the liver. It releases anger and keeps you young.

3) Come into Crow Pose. The hand position is the same as the previous exercise. Keeping the spine straight, inhale and stand up. Then exhale through the mouth as you go back down into Crow Pose. Complete one cycle every 3-4 seconds. Continue for 3-4 minutes.
This exercise works on the ankles and the meridian points there.

4) Sit with the legs stretched out in front. Grab the big toes of each foot by hooking the forefingers around the big toes and pressing the thumbs against the toenails. If you cannot reach the toes, grab your ankles. Keeping the head up throughout the exercise, inhale through the nose and stretch the spine up. Exhale through the mouth and stretch forward as far as you can. Continue for 3-4 minutes at a moderate pace. Increase your speed to a rapid pace for the last minute. Total time 4-5 minutes. Inhale, exhale and relax for 30 seconds.
This exercise works on supplying oxygen to the brain. If the head is not kept up during this exercise, it can create an undesirable pressure on the brain.

5) Lie on your back. Inhale through your nose and raise both legs up to 90°, toes pointed. Exhale through the mouth, as you bend your knees and kick the buttocks with both feet simultaneously, keeping the toes pointed. Complete one cycle every second. Continue rhythmically with powerful breathing for 2 minutes.
This exercise works on circulation.

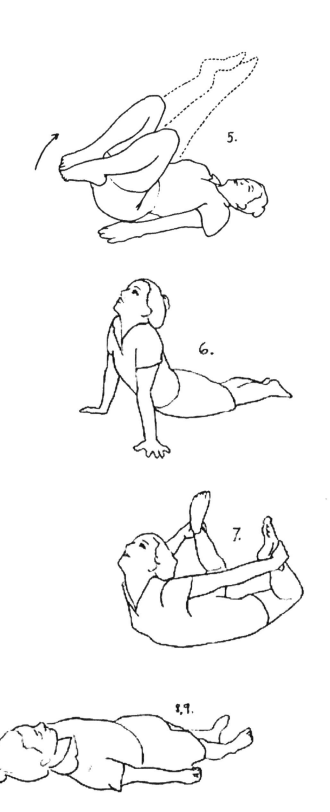

6) In Cobra Pose, lie on the stomach with the chin on the ground. The palms are flat on the floor under the shoulders; the heels are together with the soles of the feet facing up. Inhale through the nose, arching the spine up until the arms are straight and the elbows locked in Cobra Pose. Exhale through the mouth, and lower the body back down. Complete one cycle every 4 seconds. Mentally chant *Sa-Ta-Na-Ma.* Continue rhythmically, coordinating the movement with the breath and mantra for 3 minutes.
This exercise works on circulation.

7) Remaining on the stomach come into Bow Pose. Reach back, bend your knees and grab your ankles. Inhale through the nose and arch the spine completely, pulling on the ankles, so that only the pelvis, abdomen and lower chest remain on the floor, head tilted all the way back. Exhale through the mouth as you come down, bringing the thighs, shoulders and head to the floor. Complete one cycle every 2 seconds. Continue rhythmically coordinating the movement with the breath for 1-2 minutes.
This exercise works on circulation.

8) Deeply relax in Corpse Pose. Lie on your back with your arms at the sides, palms up, ankles uncrossed and eyes closed. Relax the body systematically, part by part, beginning with the feet and continuing on up to the head. Totally and consciously relax for 2 minutes.

9) Remain in Corpse Pose. Disconnect yourself from your body. Open the mouth a little and with only the power of the tongue begin to chant aloud: *Har, Har, Har, Har, Har, Har.* Chant fast, powerfully and continuously (4 repetitions of Har per second). The tongue will begin to hurt. Keep the body still. Continue for 4-5 minutes. Inhale, exhale and relax.

10) Relax completely. Feel lifeless and meditate on all weaknesses and disease leaving your body. As you deeply relax begin to sing with the recording, if available: *Aap Sahaaee Hoaa, Sache Daa Sachaa Dhoaa, Har, Har, Har.* Continue for 3-4 minutes. Then inhale and begin long deep breathing as you listen to the recording for 1-2 more minutes.

The mantra removes the animosity towards the self.

11) Sit in Easy *Pose* and sing *"Oh, That Mean, Mean Man."* Rhythmically clap your hands as you sing, or breathe long and gently, meditating at the third eye point. Continue for 10 minutes. When done in a group with wholehearted and rhythmic participation, this exercise has the ability to create a total and powerful macro-consciousness. In this macro consciousness, practice maintaining and feeling the individuality of your micro-consciousness.

12) In Easy Pose, place the arms above your head with the elbows straight and palms together. Inhale, deeply stretch the spine up and begin to pump the navel in and out powerfully for 30 seconds. Exhale, inhale and repeat two more times. Exhale and relax.

Kriya for Relaxation and Releasing Fear

1) Stand up. Bend forward from the waist, keeping the back parallel to the ground. Reach behind your legs and with your hands hold on to your calves or wherever you can comfortably reach to maintain your balance. Begin to flex the spine as in Cat/Cow Pose. Inhale and flex the spine downwards as if someone were sitting on your back. When the spine is pressed downwards the neck is arched up. Then exhale and flex your spine in the opposite direction, bringing the chin to the chest. Use the hands, knees and feet as a firm base of support for the spine to move upon. The legs must remain straight. Continue rhythmically coordinating the movement with the breath for 7 minutes.
This exercise works on the kidneys and liver.

2) Remain standing and place the hands on the hips. Rapidly begin to rotate the torso from the waist in large circles. Continue this twisting motion powerfully for 9 minutes.
This exercise rejuvenates the spleen and liver. You may feel nauseous as the liver releases toxins.

3) Sit in Easy Pose. Make fists of your hands and place them in front of you as if you were grasping a steering wheel. Begin twisting the body powerfully from side to side. Twist to your maximum. Keep the elbows up and let the neck move also. Continue for 4 minutes.
This exercise works on and exercises the kidneys.
The neck must move in order to release the blood supply to the brain.

4) Remain sitting in Easy Pose. Extend the arms up at a 60° angle, palms facing up, fingers straight and thumbs extended out. Begin to open and close the hands rapidly, bringing the tips of the fingers to the base of the palms. Continue for 7 minutes.
This exercise breaks up deposits in the fingers and prevents arthritis. If you already have arthritis, it will work on removing it.

5) Sit in Easy Pose. Extend the arms out to the sides parallel to the ground. Make fists of the hands with the thumbs tucked inside the hands touching the fleshy mound below the little finger. Inhale through the mouth and flex the elbows, bringing the fists to the shoulders. As you exhale through the mouth, straighten the arms out to the sides. Move rapidly and breathe powerfully. Continue rhythmically, coordinating the movement with the breath for 6 minutes.

This exercise removes tension from the neck and purifies the blood. In this exercise your fears will leave you when you powerfully project out on the exhale.

6) Sitting in Easy Pose assume the same hand position as in exercise 5, with the palms of the fists facing down. Stretch the arms out straight in front of you. Begin rotating the fists in small circles, the left fist counter clockwise, the right fist clockwise at the level of your heart center. Keep the elbows straight and fists tight. Move the shoulder blades and the muscles underneath the shoulder area. Continue powerfully for 2 minutes.

This exercise adjusts the muscles under the breasts. If this area is tight, it makes you very uptight.

7) Sit in Crow Pose, a crouching position with the knees drawn into the chest and the soles of the feet flat on the floor. Keep the spine straight. Make fists of the hands with the thumbs out, and place them at the level of your neck for balance. Keeping the hands stationary, inhale and stand up. Exhale and lower yourself back down to Crow Pose. Continue for 3 minutes.

8) *Sitali Pranayam:* Sit in Easy Pose and place the hands on the knees. Keep the spine straight. Curl the tongue and protrude it slightly past the lips. Inhale deeply and smoothly through the tongue and mouth. Exhale through the nose. Make the breath long and heavy. After 4-5 minutes, play the *Dukh Bhanjan* recording if available and meditate on the healing vibrations of the *Golden Temple* and the sound current of the *shabad* (song). Keep breathing rhythmically, coordinating your breath to the music. Continue for 2 minutes.

Sitali Pranayam is effective against anger, bad moods and temperament. If your mouth tastes bitter, it means you have bad breath which the pranayam will help cleanse. Dukh Bhanjan is sung in praise of the place where many were healed by a sip and dip in the nectar tank at the Golden Temple.

9) Continue listening to the recording. Sit in Easy Pose and raise the arms, curving them upwards. Close your eyes and rhythmically move your body to the music. Move as your body feels. Stop thinking and move with the beat. If you can bring your body into exact rhythm with the music, you can go into a state of ecstasy. Continue for 10 minutes.

10) Sit on the heels in Rock Pose. Place the hands on the thighs. Listen to the *Jaap Sahib* recording. Begin bowing the forehead to the floor to the *Namastang* rhythm, bowing 4 counts and resting 1 with the music. Without the recording the movement is done to 10 beats as follows: down on 1, up on 2, down on 3, up on 4, down on 5, up on 6, down on 7, up on 8, and stay up for beats 9 and 10. Continue for 8 minutes.

This exercise done in Rock Pose has been known to heal rock formations in the body such as kidney and gall-bladder stones.

11) Sit in a meditative pose. Let yourself become calm and together. Feel that you are going to achieve God's light in you. Totally remove any difference between yourself and God. Lock the hands behind the back of the head, elbows out to the sides and apply pressure, keeping the spine straight. Close your eyes and begin chanting aloud with the *Jaap Sahib* recording. Copy the very essence of it and feel the vibrations going through your hands to the back of the head as you chant. If the recording is not available breathe long and gently in this position. Continue for 8 minutes. Relax.

This exercise done in Rock Pose has been known to heal rock formations in the body such as kidney and gall-bladder stones.

Kriya for Circulation

1) Sit in Easy Pose with the fingers interlaced in Venus Lock behind the head, elbows stretched out to the sides. Inhale, exhale and bend forward touching the forehead to the ground. Inhale and sit up again. Continue for 1 minute and then begin chanting *Hum Dum Har Har, Har Har Dum Dum* in rhythm with the movement for 6 more minutes. The body will adjust itself as you move.

2) Sit in Easy Pose with the fingers interlaced in Venus Lock behind the head, elbows out to the sides. Twist right and left, breathing and moving as completely and powerfully as possible. Use the force of the elbows. Continue for 4 minutes.
This exercise works on the circulation.

3) From a sitting position, lean back on your hands. Begin an alternate push-pull motion with the legs, keeping the movements parallel to the ground and breathing in rhythm with the motion. Continue for 9 minutes.
This exercise stretches the tendons in the leg. Any pain which is experienced during this exercise is an indication of an imbalance in that area which the exercise is correcting.

4) Still leaning back on the hands, or on the elbows, stretch the legs straight up and begin scissor kicking without touching the ground. Keep the knees straight and breathe in rhythm with the movement. The legs should alternately almost touch the ground and return straight up. Continue for 3 minutes.
This exercise pressurizes the navel point and works the muscles around the hip joint.

5) Lie on the back. Raise yourself up on your elbows and soles of the feet; knees are bent with the heels directly under them. Keep the back straight. Breathe powerfully through the mouth. The head can be in any position, but the body and thighs must be in an absolutely straight line. Continue for 4 minutes. Now bring the head up and chin in, keep the buttocks up and the back straight. Breathe powerfully.

This posture adjusts the navel, works on the thighs, pushes the blood through the capillaries very quickly and helps you think and respond quickly.

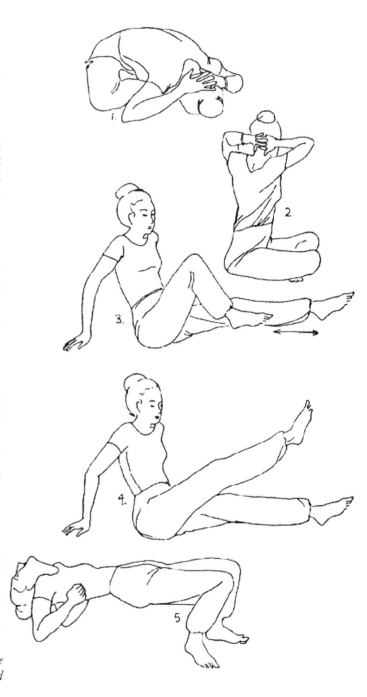

6) Come on to your hands and knees. The knees should be about shoulder width apart and the arms should be straight. Flex your spine downwards as if someone were sitting on your back. Bring the head up and back and roll the eyes up towards the sky. Put the tongue all the way out and breathe powerfully through the mouth for 2 minutes.
The eye position works on the eyesight. The tongue position helps adjust the central vagus nerve.

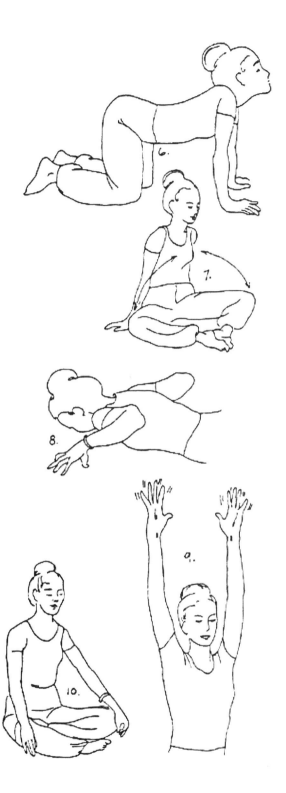

7) Sit with the soles of the feet together in Butterfly Pose. The hands are on the ground behind you, elbows straight, back straight. Alternately pull the knees up together, then drop them back to the ground, keeping the feet together. Continue for 1 minute.
This exercise works on the circulation.

8) Lie on the stomach with the fingertips on the floor under the shoulders. The heels are together with the soles of the feet facing up. Inhale into Cobra Pose, arching the spine vertebra by vertebra from the neck to the base of the spine until the arms are straight with the elbows locked. Exhale and touch the nose to the ground, bending the elbows but keeping the finger tips on the ground. Breathe powerfully and continue for 6 minutes.
This exercise works on circulation and the nervous system.

9) Sit in Easy Pose with the arms straight up, hands open, fingers stiff. Quickly vibrate the hands from the wrists; vibrate them with intensity. Continue for 4 minutes.
This exercise causes the body to adjust itself and sends blood to the capillaries of the hands to flush out circulation imbalances in this area. It has been recommended as a help for arthritis of the hands.

10) Sit perfectly in Easy Pose with the hands in Gyan Mudra. Sing with the *Jaap Sahib* recording up to *Gobinde, Mukande.* Vocally copy it exactly, or sit meditatively and breathe long and gently for 11 minutes.
This balances the right and left hemispheres of the brain,

Kriya for Mental Efficiency

1) Sit in Easy Pose with your palms about 6 inches apart in front of the heart center, fingertips pointing up. With an 8-count rhythm move as follows:

   1) Extend the right arm straight out to the side and back to the center.

   2) Extend the left arm straight out to the side and back to the center.

   3) Extend both arms straight up.

   4) Return them to the original position.

   5) Extend the right arm straight out to the side and back.

   6) Extend the left arm straight out to the side and back.

   7) Extend both arms straight out to the sides.

   8) Return the arms to the original position.

This exercise balances the frequencies of the left and right sides of the brain giving you intuition to face extraordinary circumstances.

2) Sit in Crow Pose and continue the 8-count arm movement from exercise 1. On the 3rd count stand up and on the 4th count return to Crow Pose. Continue energetically for 5 minutes.
This exercise works on the magnetic psyche.

3) Sit in Easy Pose and chant, *Praanayaam, Naam Nidhaan, Dhaan Ishnaan* for 3 minutes.
This mantra refers to the qualities of a healthy, happy, holy person: health, magnetic psyche, penetration, effectiveness, confidence and self appreciation.

4) Sit in Easy Pose with the hands in gyan mudra and chant *Ong Kar Nirankar Nirankar Ong.* The second *Ong* is emphasized and vibrated with your mouth and throat like a conch shell. The breath must come out through the nose. 3 minutes.

31.

Kriya for Intuition and Communication

1) Sit in Crow Pose, a crouching position with the soles of the feet flat on the floor. Your palms are about 6 inches apart in front of the heart center. With an 8 count rhythm, approximately 1 count per second, move as follows:

   1. Extend the right arm straight out to the side and back.

   2. Extend the left arm straight out to the side and back.

   3. Extend both arms straight up as you stand up.

   4. Return to the original position in Crow Pose.

   5. Extend the right arm straight out to the side and back .

   6. Extend the left arm straight out to the side and back .

   7. Extend both arms straight out to the sides.

   8. Return to the original position.

For one minute count with the movement. Then begin chanting *Sa-Ta-Na-Ma* in rhythm and continue for 1-2 minutes more.
This exercise will give you abundant energy.)

2) Stand with the feet shoulder-width apart and the hands on the waist. Roll your body around on the waist in large full circles for 2 minutes.
This exercise helps lower back pain, menstrual cramps and gives general flexibility.

3) Stand up with the hands on the waist and raise up onto the balls of the feet. Alternately kick the feet out keeping the knees straight. Move fast and rhythmically as you chant loudly *Hum Dum Har Har, Har Har Hum Dum.* Continue for 2 minutes.
In the art and psychology of communication, a person should be able to speak fluently even when the breath is about 40 times a minute. This exercise works towards developing that ability.

4) Continue the same movement as in exercise 3 while chanting along with the *Jaap Sahib,* if music is available . Chant loudly from the beginning; start kicking on the first *Namastang.*

Kriya for the Brain and Parathyroid

1) Sit in Easy Pose. Interlock the hands behind the neck. Keep the neck straight and begin twisting powerfully from left to right. Chant powerfully aloud: *Hari Har, Hari Har, Hari Har, Hari* with the tip of the tongue hitting the upper palate behind the teeth. One repetition every 2-3 seconds. Rhythmically coordinate the movement with the mantra for 4 minutes.
This exercise stimulates the thyroid and parathyroid glands.

2) Come into Celibate Pose, sitting between the heels with the buttocks touching the ground. Keep the spine straight. Interlace the fingers in Venus Lock behind the neck. Listen to the recording of *Jaap Sahib* and begin to bow to the *Namastang* rhythm, touching only your chin to the ground. If the recording is not available, perform the exercise in the following 10-count rhythm: down on 1, up on 2, down on 3, up on 4, down on 5, up on 6, down on 7, up on 8, remain up for 9 & 10. Continue for 15 minutes.
The posture in this exercise, also known as Bhujar Bhujang Asan, relieves problems of the reproductive area and the pituitary gland. When the chin touches the ground the parathyroid gland is stimulated. This exercise is a yogic practice guaranteed to change the total sum of oneself.

3) Sit in Easy Pose. Place the palms on the floor on each side. Keep the elbows straight. Listen to the recording *Wahe Guru, Wahe Jeeo*. Begin to rhythmically rotate the whole body, moving deep from the navel. Move with the music and when the singing begins, copy the exact sound. Continue for 15 minutes. If the recording is not available, move in the posture and breathe long and gently for 7-11 minutes.
This exercise works on the parathyroid gland and develops the power to listen.

Kriya for the Nervous System and Glandular Balance

1) Sit in Easy Pose with the arms extended straight out to the sides parallel to the ground. The palms are facing up. Begin to move only your Saturn finger (the middle finger) up and down rapidly. Using a powerful breath, inhale as you raise the finger and exhale as you lower it. Continue rhythmically, coordinating this movement with the breath for 7 minutes.

This exercise stimulates the pituitary to create a balance between the parasympathetic and sympathetic nervous systems.

2) Remain in Easy Pose. Stretch the arms out in front, parallel to the ground. Place the left hand over the right interlacing the fingers with the palms facing down. Begin to rapidly swing your arms from side to side, moving the head and neck in the same direction as the arms. Keep the elbows straight. Continue coordinating the movement with a powerful breath for 5 minutes.

This exercise prepares the body for the shock of accidents by making it very flexible. It also strengthens the chest muscle and stimulates the lymph nodes in that area. There have been reports that this exercise aids in preventing breast cancer.

3) Sitting in Easy Pose, extend the arms straight out in front, parallel to the ground. Make fists of the hands with the thumbs tucked inside touching the fleshy mound below the little finger. Keeping the arms and hands straight, bring the left arm up as the right arm goes down. Continue alternately moving the arms up and down forcefully, coordinating the movement with forceful breathing for 8 minutes.

This exercise works to balance the parathyroid gland and stimulates weight loss.

4) Butterfly Pose. Sit with the soles of the feet pressed together. Draw the feet into the groin, keeping the knees as close to the floor as possible. Interlace the fingers into Venus Lock and place the hands in the lap. Inhale and raise the arms up over the head while simultaneously drawing the knees up towards the center of the body. Exhale and lower the knees and arms down to the original position. Continue rhythmically, coordinating the movement with powerful breathing for 8 minutes.

This exercise balances the prana and apana, sets the navel point, and brings the breast line into total balance. This exercise also prepares and maintains a woman's pelvic area during her child-bearing years.

Kriya for Mind and Body Synchronization

1) Sit in Easy Pose and extend the arms straight out, palms facing forward, thumbs up and fingers straight. Rotate the hands forward so that the palms are facing backward with the thumbs touching the fleshy mound below the little fingers (mercury mound). Keep the elbows straight and rhythmically coordinate the rotation of the hands with a powerful breath of fire. Continue as powerfully as possible for 3 minutes.
This exercise works on the pituitary. It works specifically on a meridian point which helps to control one's ego.

2) Remain sitting in Easy Pose with the arms extended straight out to the sides, palms facing down. Inhale and bring the arms overhead so the palms face each other and the fingertips touch lightly. Exhale and return to the original position. Continue with powerful breaths for 3 minutes.
This exercise works on the brain.

3) Repeat exercise 1 for 1 minute.

4) Sit in Easy Pose and extend the arms straight out to the sides. Bend the wrists and rapidly move the hands up and down rhythmically coordinating the movement with a powerful breath of fire for 1 minute.
This exercise works on the nervous system.

5) Remain in Easy Pose with the arms extended out to the sides. Make fists with the thumbs touching the fleshy mound below the little fingers. Inhale and bring the fists to the shoulders by bending the elbows, exhale back coordinating the movement with a powerful breath of fire for 1 minute.
This exercise works on the ears, nose and throat.

6) Stand up. Bend the left knee and grab onto your left ankle with your left hand, and raise it up behind you. Bend forward from the hip and touch the ground with your right hand and then stand back up. Continue for 1 minute. Then change legs and continue for 1 minute.
This exercise works on balancing the hips.

7) Stand up and fold your arms at shoulder level with the arms parallel to the ground away from the chest. Begin shaking the hips rapidly from side to side while keeping the feet and upper torso stationary. 5 minutes.
This exercise stimulates the colon and aids in digestion. There may be a pain in the center of the abdomen if the colon is not moving properly; this exercise will work it out.

8) Come into Back Platform Pose. The body forms a straight line with the heels on the floor and the head up. Inhale while raising the right leg up, exhale as you lower it down. Repeat with the left leg. Continue rhythmically coordinating the movement with a powerful breath for 3 minutes.
This exercise works on the thyroid gland and strengthens the navel point. It also balances the entire hip area and prevents menstrual problems.

9) Sit in Crow Pose, crouching with the soles of the feet flat on the floor. The arms are in front of you for balance. Sing *"America the Beautiful,"* or breathe slowly and deeply for 4 minutes.

10) Lie on the back and arch up into Wheel Pose. Start with the knees bent with the soles of the feet flat on the floor. Bend the elbows, place the palms of the hands on the floor under the shoulders with the fingers pointing backward toward the shoulders. Inhale and carefully raise the buttocks so that the body forms one continuous arch from the heels to the palms of the hands. In this position sing *"America the Beautiful"* or breathe slowly and deeply for 1 minute.

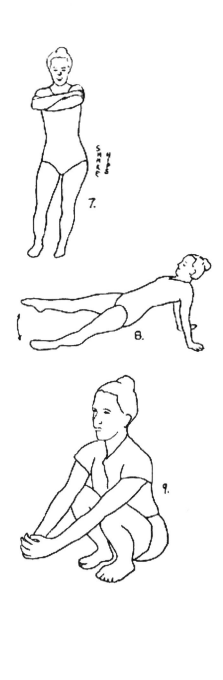

Kriya for Building the Nervous System

1) Sit in Easy Pose with the arms straight out to the sides and the palms facing up. Open and close the hands, moving only your four fingers and not your thumbs. Begin breath of fire. Inhale as the hands close, exhale as the hands open. Continue rhythmically coordinating the movement of the hands with powerful breathing for 4 minutes. Then continue the movement with the palms facing down for 1 minute more.
This exercise works on the brain. The control system for the brain is located in the fingertips.

2) In Easy Pose extend the arms straight out to the sides and parallel to the ground. Place the thumbs inside the hands and make the hands into fists. Alternately, cross the arms in front and back of the head, returning to the original position between each movement. Continue rhythmically coordinating the movement with powerful breathing for 4 minutes.
This exercise works on the lymph nodes and removes calcium deposits from the shoulder area.

3) Remain sitting and extend the legs and arms straight out in front of you, parallel to each other with the hands flat and the thumbs locked together. Keeping the head up with a straight spine and no bend in the elbows or knees stretch forward as you exhale and return upright as you inhale. Continue with fast, powerful breathing for 4 minutes.
This exercise works on putting the body into proper alignment.

4) Sit with the legs stretched out in front of you. Place the palms on your temples keeping the fingers together and the thumbs separate. Point the hands away from the front of the face. Begin twisting the whole upper body from left to right. Continue with powerful breathing, inhaling left and exhaling right for 2 minutes.
This exercise works on removing calcium deposits from the shoulders and neck. You may feel pain in the armpits, where the balance of parasympathetic and sympathetic nervous systems is adjusted.

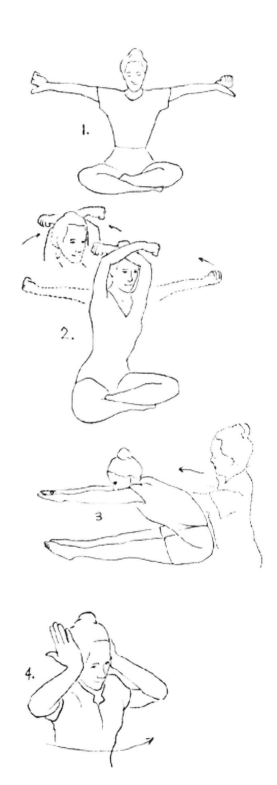

5) Remain sitting with the legs stretched out in front of you. Come into Yoga Mudra by interlacing the fingers in Venus Lock behind the back, keeping the elbows straight. Inhale in 4 parts as you bend forward, raising your arms up as high as possible. Exhale in one breath as you return upright. Continue rhythmically coordinating the movement and breath for 2 minutes. *This exercise gives endurance and grit.*

6. Stand up with the hands locked behind you in Venus Lock as before. Lower yourself down as though you were sitting in a chair of standard height and stay there. Inhale in 4 counts and bend forward, raising your arms up behind you. Exhale in one breath and return to the original upright sitting position. Continue rhythmically coordinating the movement and breath for 2 minutes. *This exercise works on the knees.*

7) Sit down with the left leg stretched out straight in front of you. Place the sole of the right foot firmly against the inside of the left thigh so that the heel creates a closure in front of the genital area. Reach forward and catch the left toe or foot, whichever is more comfortable. Pull the neck back and bend forward as you exhale. Inhale and come up. Continue with powerful breathing for 3 minutes. Then inhale, change legs and continue for 3 minutes more. *This exercise is for the spine. The closure or "gate" which the heel creates in front of the genital area allows the body to remove toxins.*

8) Sit in Easy Pose. Fold the arms, right over left, hands grasping the biceps. Rock forward slightly and bounce up and down on the buttocks like a jumping bean. Jump hard and breathe powerfully for 4 minutes. *This exercise works on breaking up deposits and unwanted fat in the body. It stimulates the circulation and builds strength in the spine to resist injury in case of trauma.*

9) Remain sitting in Easy Pose with the hands folded at the chest in Prayer Mudra. Chant with *Jaap Sahib*, copying the sound exactly until the recording reaches *Gobinde, Mukande.* If the recording is not available, breathe slowly and deeply for 7-11 minutes. *This exercise works on cleansing the mind.*

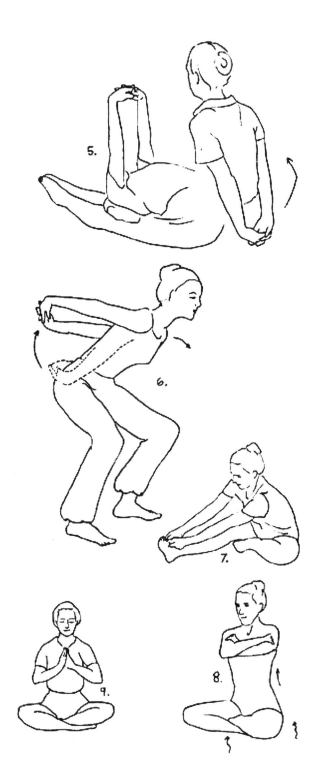

Kriya for State of Mind and Paranoia

1) Sit in Easy Pose. Extend the arms straight out to the sides, parallel to the ground. Close the hands, bringing the fingertips to the base of the palm and lock them there. Straighten the thumbs. Keep the spine straight, chest out and chin in. Begin fully rotating the hands at the wrists with the thumbs moving from up and back to down and back, maintaining a tight grip of the fingers. Continue rhythmically with heavy powerful breathing for 7-8 minutes.
This exercise works on the pituitary and breaking through one's paranoia.

2) Assume the same posture as in exercise 1. Inhale and bring the thumbs toward the shoulders, but not quite touching them. Exhale and return to the original position.. Continue with powerful breathing for 2 minutes.
This exercise stimulates the pituitary gland.

3) Remain sitting in Easy Pose. Place the hands on the knees. Keeping the chin tucked in and the neck tense and hard as steel, begin flexing the spine. Inhale, arching back slightly and pulling the chest and neck up. Then exhale arching forward slightly while pushing the chin out. One complete cycle takes 1-2 seconds. Continue for 4 minutes.
This exercise stimulates the balance of the thyroid and parathyroid glands thus promoting quick weight loss. If this exercise is done correctly it will keep one looking young.

4) Sit in Easy Pose. Inhale, extending the arms straight out to the sides, parallel to the ground, palms facing up. Exhale and bring the hands to the shoulders. From this position inhale and raise both elbows towards your head, lifting the shoulders and entire spine up. Exhale and lower the elbows. One complete cycle takes 2 seconds. Continue rhythmically, coordinating this 4-part movement with powerful breathing while mentally chanting *Har, Har, Har, Har* for 3-4 minutes.

5) Lie flat on your back with your arms relaxed at your sides. Put your heels together and raise them 6 inches off the floor. Keep the knees straight and toes forward. In this position begin breathing powerfully, long and deep from the navel point. Continue for 2-3 minutes.
This exercise works on the lower abdomen and navel area.

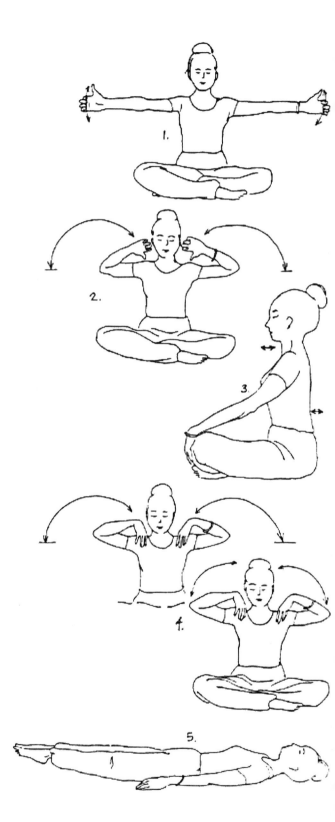

6) Remain lying flat on your back. Place the hands under the buttocks palms down and cross your legs at the ankles, keeping them straight. Inhale and raise both legs up to 90°. Exhale and lower the legs. If one side becomes tired, you may reverse the cross of your legs at the ankle. Rhythmically move with powerful breathing for 3 minutes.
This exercise works on removing excess water from the body.

7) Lying flat on the back, spread the legs apart. Raise both arms straight up with the palms facing towards your feet. Inhale, exhale, and sit up touching the toes with the hands. Then inhale and lower yourself back down. Rhythmically coordinating the movement with the breath for 6 minutes.
This exercise works on the pelvic bone. It also removes feelings of paranoia and lets you feel absolutely free.

8) Come into Bridge Pose. Begin in a sitting position with the legs straight out. Lean back slightly, supporting the upper torso with the arms locked at the elbows and the palms flat on the floor. Bend the knees, draw the feet in towards the buttocks with the soles flat against the floor and raise the buttocks so that the body is parallel to the ground, head up. The arms and lower legs should be at right angles to the body. Now powerfully move the body up and down. 3-4 minutes.
This exercise works on the buttocks and the hips and helps to keep you young.

9) Assume the same posture as exercise 8 but with the head back, parallel to the body. Stick your tongue out and begin breathing heavily in Reverse Lion Pose. Continue for 1-2 minutes. Now purr like a lion, vibrating the back of the tongue as though you were gargling. Continue powerfully for 1 minute.
This exercise is a preventative against the common cold.

10) Sit in Easy Pose. Sing the song *"Nobility"* for 4-5 minutes or breathe slowly and deeply.

11) Sitting in Easy Pose, interlace the fingers into open Venus Lock with the thumb tips touching and pointing back. Raise the arms overhead forming an arcline/halo. Focus your eyes at the tip of your nose and breathe through the navel point. Listen to *Jaap Sahib* and begin copying the sound exactly or breathe long and gently. Continue for 9 minutes until *Charpat chand tav prasaad.*

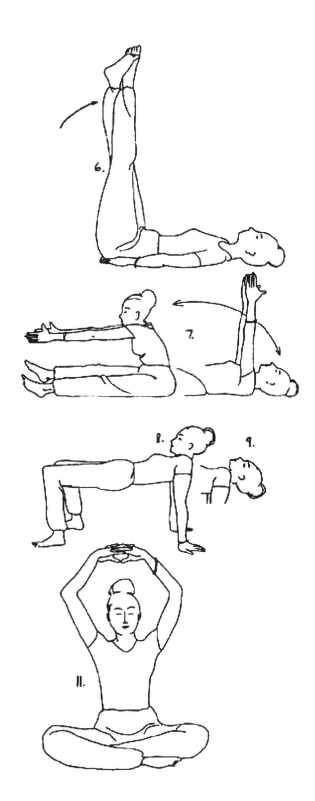

Kriya for Balancing the Brain

These "mirror exercises" are most effective if done with mirrors. Ultimately you make a mental mirror and do them.

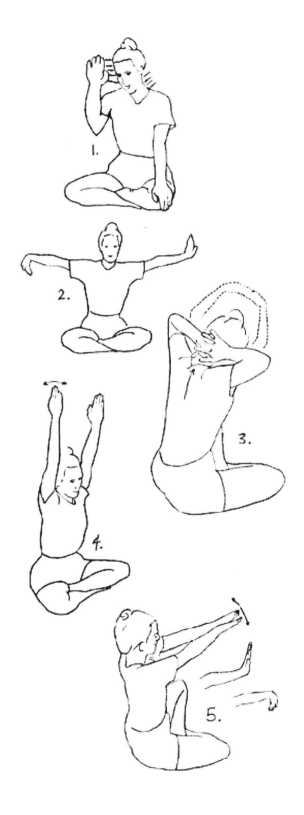

1) Sit in Easy Pose. Place the right hand with the palm facing in. The left hand rests on the knee. Begin vibrating the right hand from the wrist in 2-3 jerking movements from the front of the jaw area back to the temples. There will be tremendous tension in the neck and forehead. The head and hand should move at the same time with the same strength. Tension will move the head and strength will move the hand. The ears will feel extreme pressure and your hearing will become temporarily disconnected if done correctly. Relax briefly after the completion of each cycle. At this time your hearing will return to normal. 7 minutes.
This exercise reduces anger and the trauma of birth.

2) Sitting in Easy Pose, extend the arms straight out to the sides, parallel to the ground, palms facing down. Begin bending the hands at the wrists, one hand goes up as the other one goes down. Then straighten the hands and reverse the movement. Keep the arms very straight and move powerfully, putting your total strength into it. There will be tension under the chin, causing you to shake a little. Continue for 5 minutes.
This exercise neutralizes the left and right hemispheres of the brain.

3) In Easy Pose, interlace your fingers in Venus Lock behind the neck. Keep the chin in and chest out. Rapidly raise the arms straight up overhead, palms down, and then lower them to the original position. Continue with powerful breathing for 3 minutes.
This exercise works on breaking up the deposits in the shoulders. It also works on the arteries, specifically the main arteries to the brain.

4) In Easy Pose stretch the arms straight up, palms facing each other, fingers together, thumbs separate. Keep the arms stiff and move the hands back and forth in opposite directions 6-9 inches. 4 minutes.
This exercise improves the balance in the hemispheres of the brain. If done correctly, the whole body will adjust itself.

5) In Easy Pose extend the arms straight in front of you, palms down, fingers together. Bend the hands straight up at the wrists and return them to the original position, then bend the hands down and then return to the original position. Move powerfully for 3 minutes.

6) Sit in Easy Pose. Place your arms behind your back and interlace the fingers into Venus Lock. Swing the arms powerfully, twisting from side to side. Move rapidly for 3 minutes.

This exercise works on the liver.

7) Sit in Easy Pose. Extend the arms straight out to either side, parallel to the ground, palms facing down. Keeping the elbows straight, begin flapping the arms up and down for 3 counts (A). On the count of 4, clap the hands over the head (B). Continue with breath of fire for 7 minutes.

This exercise is very stimulating and good for the chest muscles. It specifically works on the lymph area and removes toxins from the body.

8) Sit in Easy Pose. Extend the arms straight out in front and clap the hands (A). Then swing the arms back and up, clapping the hands over and behind the head (B). Continue moving rhythmically and powerfully for 3 minutes.

This exercise works on adjusting the ribs.

9) Sitting down, lean back and place your hands on the floor behind you, supporting the weight of your body. Bend the legs, keep the knees slightly apart and the calf muscles tight. Rapidly begin kicking the buttocks with alternate feet. Continue kicking powerfully for 7 minutes.

This exercise works on the often unused muscles of the buttocks and breaks up any deposits which may have accumulated there. It also opens up the capillaries releasing the blood supply to the legs and feet.

10) Sit in Easy Pose. Place the hands on the knees. Alternately bend from left to right bringing the head down to the knee. Come all the way up and bend all the way down. Continue rhythmically for 4 minutes.

This exercise works on the hips and eliminates gas. It also removes toxins from the spleen.

11) Sitting in Easy Pose, stretch your arms up overhead with the palms together and the thumbs crossed. The arms are straight and hugging the ears. Keep the chin in and chest out. Listen to the *"Dukh Bhanjan"* recording and sing, copying the sound perfectly. Sing loudly with an open heart. If the recording is not available breathe long and gently. Continue for 20 minutes with the recording, 7-11 minutes without it.

The posture in this exercise is a perfect Prayer Pose. It is very difficult to speak in this posture. Once you are able to speak, it will open up your heart and you will be able to conquer death. "When you sing and pray with an open heart, the prayer becomes your power. Your power becomes ingrained in you and you become ingrained in the power. Then nothing can touch you. "

Kriya for the Nervous System

1) Sit in Easy Pose. Place the hands at your sides with the knuckles and forefingers resting on the floor for support. Inhale through the mouth and arch the spine forward, lift the neck up and push the chin and chest out. Then exhale through the mouth and arching the spine back, bring the chin into the chest. Continue with powerful breathing for 4 minutes.

This exercise opens up the lungs and works on removing anger, grief and insecurities. It also enhances alertness and clarity of mind and prevents senility.

2) Remain sitting in Easy Pose. Place the hands in front of the neck with the palms facing each other, 4-6 inches apart, on the count of 1. On the count of 2, move the hands out to the shoulders with the palms at a diagonal to the body. On the count of 3, straighten the arms out parallel to the ground with the palms facing down to the sides. Then on the count of 4, return the hands to the shoulders with the palms at a diagonal to the body. Continue this sequence keeping the fingers stiff and the movements tight and precise. Move rapidly and powerfully for 11 minutes.

This exercise works on the message system of the brain.

3) In Easy Pose, extend both arms straight out to the sides with the palms facing up. Keeping the hands and arms straight, and moving lightly, raise them up over the head without touching the palms together. Then lower them as though a ton of weight is coming down. The chin and neck should come up about 1½ inches as you raise the arms. Continue moving rapidly and breathing powerfully for 4 minutes.

This exercise removes deposits from the neck.

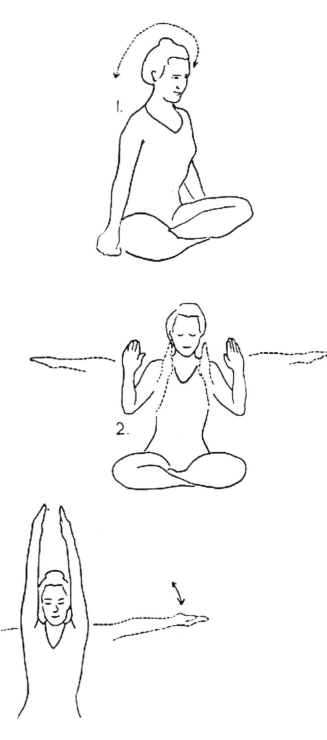

4) Lie on the stomach with the palms flat on the floor under the shoulders. The heels are together with the soles of the feet facing up. Inhale into Cobra Pose, arching the spine from the neck to the base of the spine until the arms are straight with the elbows locked. Begin kicking the buttocks with alternate heels. Move quickly and powerfully. Continue for 6 minutes.

This exercise works on the knees, which control much of the body's tissues. When the knees are not kept in shape they can be the cause of brain tumors and extra growths in the arteries and the intestinal tract.

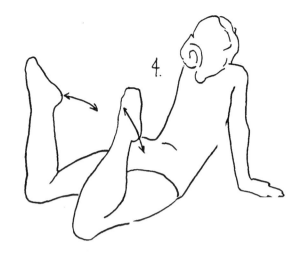

5) Sit in Crow Pose, a squatting position with the feet flat on the floor. Interlace the fingers into Venus Lock and place them behind the neck. Open the chest wide and bounce up and down in Crow Pose for 3 counts. On the count of 4, stand up and then lower yourself back into Crow Pose in time for the count of 1 without breaking the rhythm. Continue for 4 minutes.

This exercise gives a woman absolute control over her sexual organs.

6) Stand up and stretch the arms straight up over the head, arms hugging the ears. Place the palms in Prayer Mudra with the thumbs crossed. While stretching, begin chanting *Har, Har, Har, Har...* continuously with the tip of the tongue hitting the upper palate behind the teeth. Continue for 2 minutes. Inhale and stretch the whole body powerfully. Exhale and relax.

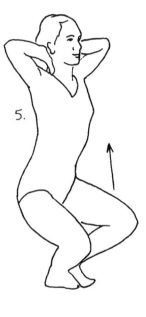

44.

Kriya for the
Frontal Brain

1) Sit in Easy Pose. Place the hands on the knees. Arch the spine forward and push the lower jaw out, pushing the teeth out as the head goes up. Then arch the spine back and open the mouth. Flex your entire spine and breathe powerfully through the mouth. Continue for 3-4 minutes.
This exercise works on the frontal brain.

2) Sit in Crow Pose, a squatting position with the feet flat on the floor, knees apart. Place the hands on the waist. Inhale through the mouth and push the lower jaw forward, pushing the teeth out as you stand up. Then open the mouth and exhale through it as you lower yourself back down into Crow Pose. Continue for 2-3 minutes.
This exercise works on the meridian points in the thigh, which are connected with sexual energy and compassion. The thigh bone controls the balance of potassium and calcium, and the inflow and outflow of energy.

3) Sit down in Easy Pose with the forearms bent up at the sides, hands at face level. The palms face out, away from each other, about 14 inches apart. Bring the right forearm out, straightening the arm so that it is parallel to the ground, palm down. Then return to the original position and repeat with the left arm. Continue alternating arms fast and hard for 6 minutes.
This exercise pressurizes the frontal brain at the third eye point.

4) Remain in Easy Pose, with the hands above the shoulders in fists, the thumbs locked inside pressing on the mound of the little finger. The movements are in a 4 count rhythm as follows:
   1) Bring the right arm out and up 60° and then return to the original position.
   2) Bring the left arm out and up 60° and then return to the original position.
   3) Bring both arms straight up over the head, parallel to each other.
   4) Return them to the original position.
Continue this rhythm moving fast and powerfully for 6-7 minutes.

5) In Easy Pose stretch your arms straight out parallel to the ground with the palms facing up. Bend the middle (Saturn) fingers into the palms and lock your thumbs over them. The other fingers are straight. Pump the arms up and down 12 inches above and 12 inches below the original position. The breath will flow in rhythm with the motion. Keep the elbows straight and move fast and powerfully for 3 minutes.

This breaks up deposits in the neck that block circulation to the brain. It works on patience, the quality of the Saturn finger.

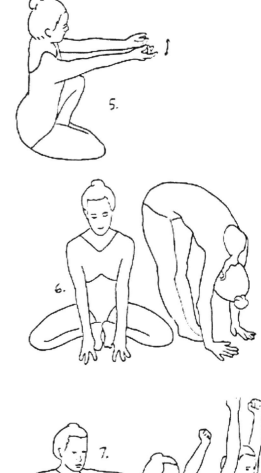

6) Come into Frog Pose, squatting so the buttocks are resting on the heels, which are off the ground and touching. The fingertips are on the ground between the knees, and the head is up. Inhale and raise the buttocks high. Exhale and come down to the starting position and let the buttocks strike the heels. Breathe deeply and powerfully, and continue until you have done 54 cycles, approximately 2-3 minutes.

7) Come into Rock Pose, sitting on your heels with the tops of the feet on the ground. In this position, repeat the arm movements of exercise 4 for 2 minutes.

This exercise works on the digestion and the removal of deposits and toxins in the breast area.

8) Stand up and dance to Don Cooper's *Twelve Months*. Close your eyes and move every muscle of the body without moving far from your spot. Flow with the rhythm, mirroring the notes and words with body language. Continue for 25 minutes.

This natural dancing instinct gives the body a chance to release deposited toxins. Effective communication uses body language to express and project the words we speak. Those who do not express their psyche through the vibration of the body will fail in communication and action.

Kriya for Metabolic Change

1) Sit in Easy Pose. The arms are at the sides, with the elbows bent down and the forearms parallel to the body. The palms are facing each other at the level of the head and the fingers are together, pointing up. Begin moving alternate arms up and out at a 60° angle and then back to the original position. It is not necessary for the arms to be totally straight when extended, but it is important to do it as fast as possible, breathing with the rhythm. The head will move powerfully in rhythm with the arm movement. Continue for 6 minutes.

This exercise increases the blood supply to the brain. When it is done very fast, it will stimulate chemical reactions in the body which will help maintain youthfulness.

2) Remain in Easy Pose. Stretch your arms straight out in front of you at a 45° angle to each other with the elbows locked. The hands are angled slightly away from each other, palms facing and fingers outstretched, as if holding a very large ball. Rotate the arms very rapidly, inscribing small circular motions in the air. The right arm moves clockwise, the left counterclockwise. Keep the hands very straight. Continue for 4 minutes.

This exercise works on the brain and its capacity to produce chemicals which increase responsiveness.

3) Repeat exercise 1 for 3 minutes.

4) Repeat exercise 2 for 1 minute.

5) Still in Easy Pose, make fists of your hands with the thumbs out and bring your arms up to chest level, elbows out, forearms parallel to the floor. Begin pounding your chest vigorously and as fast as possible, alternating the fists. You will create a thumping rhythm at the level of the heart. Continue for 5 minutes.

This exercise works on the lymph meridians and the pineal gland to stimulate metabolic change. It releases the stress of extreme grief or anger.

6) Repeat exercise 1 for 1 minute.

7) Repeat exercise 2 for 2 minutes.

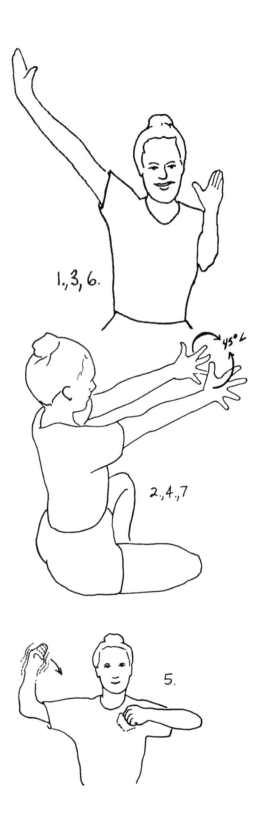

8) Remain in Easy Pose. Stretch your arms straight out from the sides at shoulder level, palms down. Begin flapping the arms up and down from the shoulders, imitating a bird's wings and adding a flapping movement of the hands at the wrists. The chant which accompanies this exercise is *Har Har Har Har* in rhythm with each up or down movement of the arms. Make sure that the tip of the tongue hits the upper palate behind the teeth with every repetition of the mantra. Continue for 2 minutes.

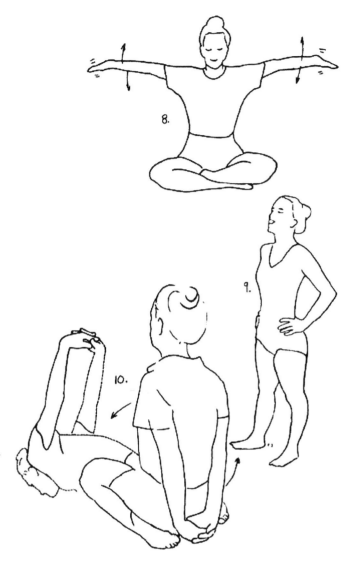

9) Come standing. Put on some dancing music which is meditative and enjoyable. Don Cooper's *"Twelve months"* recording was used in this class. With your eyes closed, begin expressing each musical note with body language. "You must sing; you must dance; you must express and you must keep your eyes closed!" Continue for 20 minutes.
This exercise works on the experience of projectability and effective grace. Meditative dance has the capacity to give you spontaneous fearlessness.

10) This exercise is performed to the recording of *Jaap Sahib*. Sit on the heels in Rock Pose. Interlace the fingers into Venus Lock behind your back. Moving in perfect rhythm with the music, bring your forehead to the ground on the accented beat of *Namastang* as your arms extend straight up behind your back in Yoga Mudra. Return to the upright position by the second accented beat of the phrase. Continue in rhythm for the length of *Jaap Sahib*, which is 29 minutes, or follow a 10 count rhythm as follows: down on 1, up on 2, down on 3, up on 4, down on 5, up on 6, down on 7, up on 8, then remain up for beats 9 and 10.
This exercise accompanied by the recording will build stamina and inexhaustible energy.

Kriya for the Upper Body, Neck and Shoulders

1) Come sitting in Easy Pose. Stretch the arms out from the shoulders in front of the body with the hands turned so that the palms remain facing out throughout the exercise. From this position bring the arms straight out from the sides of the body. In the third position, swing the arms straight out behind the body, extending them as far as possible while keeping the arms straight. Then return the arms to the second position, extending out from the sides and repeat the 4-step movement. The mantra to be chanted with the exercise is *Sa-Ta-Na-Ma* corresponding to the movements for 3 minutes.
This exercise works on the muscles of the upper arm.

2) Remain in Easy Pose. Using alternate arms reach straight up and pull straight down fast and powerfully as if ringing church bells in rhythm. While the arms come down the hands are in fists, thumbs out. As the arms go up the fingers will stretch up and reach to pull down. The arms move in parallel lines 8-12 inches apart. Exhale with each downward movement. Continue for 30 minutes.

3) Repeat exercise 1 for 2 minutes.

4) Still in Easy Pose, sit with the spine straight, arms at your sides. Put your hands in fists on the ground, on the knuckles with the thumbs out. Begin twisting the body from side to side, keeping the head straight. Rotate alternate shoulders forward, inhaling as you twist to the left, exhaling as you twist to the right. After 3 minutes begin chanting *Hum Dum Har Har*, each syllable corresponding to one twist. Continue chanting with the movement for 30 seconds more.
This exercise works to break up calcium deposits as well as adjusting the ribcage and lower vertebra of the neck.

5) Remain in Easy Pose. The arms are extended straight out to the sides and down 30° from the shoulders with the palms up. Swing both arms together up over the head and down again, as fast as possible. The palms do not touch over the head nor do the hands touch the ground. Inhale as the arms come up and exhale as they come down. Continue for 3 minutes.
This exercise strengthens the nervous system and breaks up calcium deposits.

6) Remain in Easy Pose with the hands on the knees. Lean the head all the way back and begin rolling the head in half circles, first to one shoulder, then back and around to the other shoulder, with a full stretch. Continue for 2 minutes.
This exercise breaks up the calcium deposits in the neck.

49.

Kriya for the Ribcage Area

1) Come sitting in Easy Pose with the arms stretched straight out in front of you parallel to the ground 12-18 inches apart. The thumb and little finger are touching and the palms are down. Swing your arms straight up over your head on the inhale, and then swing them down towards the ground on the exhale. Make sure that your arms and hands don't touch either your body or the ground. Swing powerfully for 8 minutes.
This exercise adjusts the rib cage and relaxes this area.

2) Still in Easy Pose, cross your arms and fold them around your chest, as if hugging yourself. The hands are gripping tightly to the lower ribs. In this position begin twisting the torso and head from side to side fast and powerfully, inhaling as you twist left and exhaling as you twist right. Continue for 3 minutes.
This exercise moves the diaphragm area and works on the stomach.

3) Come sitting on your heels. Reach back with your hands, firmly grasping your heels or ankles, and then arch up into Camel Pose. Your weight rests on your straight arms and upper legs, and your navel point and hips are up as high as possible, while your head drops back. In this position begin a heavy and powerful breath of fire, pumping your navel powerfully with each exhale. Continue for 4 minutes. Relax for 2 minutes.
This exercise adjusts the navel point and relieves the stomach from the effects of overeating. The heavy breath of fire cleanses the body of disease if practiced regularly. The exercise gives control over hunger and thirst.

4) Return to Easy Pose. Bring your arms up in a circle above your head with the hands slightly cupped. From this position, bring your arms down so that they form a circle from the shoulders down. Continue this motion, inhaling as your arms come up and exhaling as they come down. After 2-3 minutes, begin singing *"All Things Come from God and All Things Go To God,"* moving in perfect rhythm with the music, or continue the breathing pattern. Sing from the heart and let your hands dance. Continue for 20 minutes.
This exercise develops the flow of the psyche.

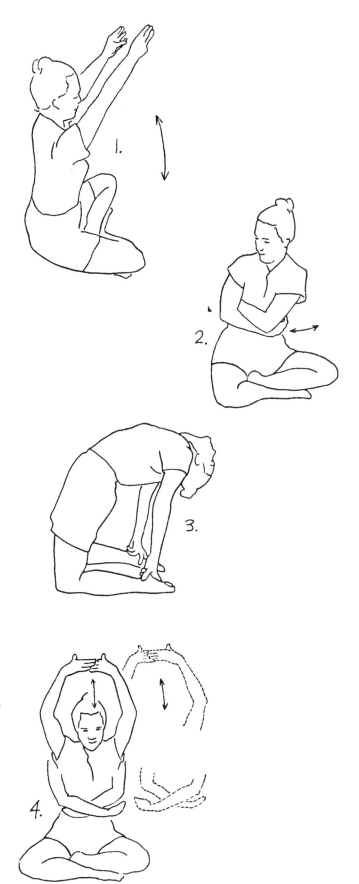

Kriya for the Frontal Lobe of the Brain

1) Sit in Easy Pose with your hands on your knees. The chest is out and the shoulders are back. Maintaining this posture, begin vibrating the front of the face, using a very rapid and short up and down vibrating motion. Try to move just the forehead. The breath will adjust itself. Continue for 8-9 minutes.
This exercise is called Mastak Subhaee. It works on the change and replacement of gray matter in the brain.

2) Remain in Easy Pose with the hands on the knees. Begin rolling the head in the shape of a figure eight. The chin comes down to the center of the chest with each circle. Make sure that the exercise is performed steadily with equal timing for each revolution of the head. Continue for 3 minutes at a moderate pace and then sit still for 30 seconds.
This exercise is called Infinity Kriya. It is very powerful and must be done carefully and consciously. The effect is to balance the central ear which affects clear and conscious thought.

3) Still in Easy Pose, bring the arms straight out from the sides of the body at shoulder level, the hands in fists with the thumbs outside. Inhale and bring both fists in to the top of the shoulders while stretching the elbows out as powerfully as possible and flexing your biceps. Return to the original position on the exhale. Continue the motion for 9 minutes. The musical recording of *Sukhmanee Sahib* accompanied this exercise in the class.

4) Remain in Easy Pose. Still listening to *Sukhmanee Sahib,* stretch the arms straight out in front and upwards at a 45° angle with the palms facing down, fingers held together on each hand. In this position begin shaking the head as fast as possible in a very short sideways motion. Shake the skull in a continuous motion for 1 minute. Inhale and relax.

Kriya for Balancing Head and Heart

1) Sit in Easy Pose, arms straight out to the sides from the shoulders with the hands bent up at the wrists at a 90° angle, palms facing out and fingers together. The movement is in 4 parts, starting with this position. On count 2 rotate the hands at the wrists so that the fingers point straight forward. On count 3 return to the original position, and on count 4 rotate the wrists so that the fingers point straight backwards. The elbows will rotate. Move in a rhythm of one full cycle per 4 seconds. Keep the arms straight and continue for 6-7 minutes, inhaling and exhaling with the movements. *This exercise changes the chemistry of the brain fluid.*

2) Still in Easy Pose, extend the arms straight out to the sides parallel to the floor, palms facing out. In the first part of the exercise, inhale as the arms are raised up to form an arc with the palms crossing over and slightly in front of the top of the head without touching. Lower the arms to the original position as you exhale, and then raise the arms again as you inhale, this time cross the palms over and slightly *behind* the head. Continue the motion powerfully for 1-2 minutes.

3) Stand up and add Crow squats to the arm movements of exercise 2. As you exhale come down into Crow Pose, a crouching position with the knees drawn into the chest and soles of the feet flat on the floor. As you inhale and bring the arms up over the head, come into a standing position. Continue alternately squatting in Crow Pose and standing up with the arm movement for 3-4 minutes at a speed of 1 second per movement.

Sahib Parnaam Kriya

This entire Kriya is done to the recording of Jaap Sahib. The exercises give tremendous energy, intuition and mental clarity.

1) Begin the music and lie down on your stomach and meditate on the words until the rhythmic part of the music begins (about 1 minute). Then come up into Triangle Pose, placing your weight on the balls of your feet and your palms. Your head hangs down. Exhaling from this position, bend the arms slightly and bring the forehead to the ground on the accented beat of *Namastang*. Return to triangle pose on the accented beat of *Akaale*, as you inhale. Make sure that you move in perfect rhythm with the music. The legs remain totally straight, heels together, while the arms will bend and straighten as you switch positions. Continue in this way until the recording reaches *Gobinde, Mukande, Udaare, Apaare, Hariang, Kariang, Nirnaame, Akaame* (approximately 15 minutes).

If the music is not available, perform the movements in the following ten-count rhythm: down on 1, up on 2, down on 3, up on 4, down on 5, up on 6, down on 7, up on 8, and remain up for counts 9 and 10. (One cycle takes about 10 seconds.)
This is called Saram Parnaam which can perfect the function of the brain and glandular system and clear up facial blemishes.

2) Still listening to the music, come into Tree Pose standing straight with the arms overhead in an arc with the palms and fingers touching in Prayer Mudra. Bend one knee to the side and bring the other leg up so that the foot lies flat against the inner thigh as high as possible. Balance in this position, changing legs if desired, until the recording reaches *Ek Achree Chand* (approximately 12 minutes).
This exercise strengthens the side muscles of the spine and brings total spinal balance to protect from the effects of sudden shock.

3) While the recording continues, come sitting in Easy Pose with the hands in Gyan Mudra. The arms and spine are very straight. In this position chant precisely with the recording in perfect frequency from the navel point, copying the sound exactly. Or breathe long and gently until the recording ends (about 2 minutes).
This exercise is called Yoga Parnaam.

Kriya for the Nervous System and Balancing the Blood

1) Stand up with your legs about 2 feet apart. Your upper arms are parallel to the floor with the forearms bent parallel to the body, palms forward, fingers spread. Bend the knees and come into Crow Pose, feet flat on the floor, then return to a standing position. Continue this movement with 8 breaths of fire for each movement down and 8 for each movement up. 4-5 minutes.

This exercise adjusts the sexual nervous system in relationship to the bone marrow. It will change the blood chemistry and balance the nervous system and circulation.

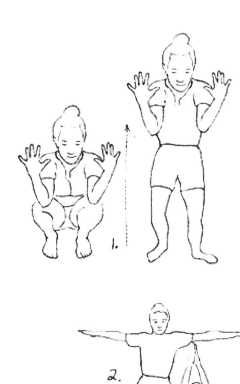

2) Remain standing and begin Jumping Jacks, coordinating the movement so that the legs are together while the arms are stretched out to the sides parallel to the ground. When the legs are spread apart, the arms are overhead, hands clapping. Continue at a rate of one complete cycle per second, with a powerful breath, for 4-5 minutes.

3) Still standing, spread the legs and extend the arms straight out to the sides, parallel to the ground. Begin doing windmills, alternately touching the left hand to the right toes as the other arm stretches straight up, and vice-versa. Make sure that you straighten the spine between stretches. Continue at a fast pace for 1-2 minutes.

4) Quickly sit down in Easy Pose and sing the chorus of *"The Khalsa Way"* for 2-3 minutes or breathe long and gently for 2-3 minutes.

Kriya for Balancing the Aura

1) Sit in Easy Pose. Bend your elbows out to the sides at shoulder level and slightly cross your hands in front of your open eyes. Spread your fingers wide, like a fan. Then move your upper arms from the elbow, bringing the hands slightly out to the side and back again. The upper arm will be parallel to the floor. Continue this motion rapidly and forcefully for 3 minutes.

This exercise works on the eyes.

2) Stand up in Archer Pose, with the right leg bent, knee over the toes. The left leg is straight back with the foot flat on the ground at a 45° angle to the front foot. Raise the right arm straight in front, parallel to the ground and make a fist as if grasping a bow. Pull the left arm back as if the pulling the bowstring back from the shoulder. Face forward with the eyes fixed on the horizon above the fist. Now begin bending the right knee so the body drops down, and then come back up to the original position. Continue this motion rhythmically for 2 minutes. Switch sides and continue for 2 more minutes. Switch sides and continue for 30 seconds more.

3) Come into Cobra Pose. Lie down on the stomach with the palms flat on the floor under the shoulders and the heels together with the soles of the feet facing up. Arch the spine from the neck to the base until the arms are straight with the elbows locked. From Cobra Pose raise the buttocks up into the air into Triangle Pose supporting yourself on your palms and your feet. Then return to position Cobra Pose and alternate movements at a speed of 2 seconds per posture for 5 minutes.

4) Sit in Easy Pose and play the recording of *Wahe Guru Jeeo*. When you hear the words *Wahe Guru* or *Wahe Jeeo*, pull *Muhl Bhand* for the length of the phrase, then relax and meditate on the words in between. When you hear *Toohee*, do powerful breath of fire, then relax and meditate in between. Continue for at least one cycle of the meditation, approximately 14 minutes.

This meditation moves the energy from the 3rd chakra out into the aura, and returns to the 3rd chakra energizing each chakra. If you practice it for the full length of the recording for 90 days, you will perfect the meditation.

Appendix

Mantras

A mantra is a series of sounds which have been designed to elevate or modify consciousness through their meaning and rhythmical repetition. It is beneficial in Kundalini Yoga to link a mantra to the breath. This technique helps to focus the mind and strengthen the endurance during challenging exercises.

Sat Nam: This is the *bij* or seed mantra that is most widely used in the practice of Kundalini Yoga. It is a universal mantra, representing the vibration of truth; *Sat* means truth, the reality of existence, and *Nam* means name or identity, our connection with the truth.

Sa-Ta-Na-Ma: This is the *Panj Shabad*, expressing the five primal sounds of the universe. It is the nuclear form of *Sat Naam*. *Sa* means Infinity, *Ta*, life, *Na*, death and *Ma*, rebirth. The fifth sound is the `A' that is the common connecting sound, meaning "to come."

Wahe Guru, Wahe Guru, Wahe Guru, Wahe Jeeo: Wahe Guru is the Guru mantra. It is the mantra of the complete and total infinity of ecstasy, the experience of coming from the darkness to the light. The word *Jeeo* sends the message directly to the soul.

Har: This word represents the Creative Infinity.

Hari Har: The word *Hari* represents the action and flow of Creative Infinity. The mantra moves from the action to the being of Creative Infinity.

Hum Dum Har Har: This mantra opens the heart chakra, the center of compassion. It is often chanted as *Hum Dum Har Har Har Har Hum Dum.*

Aap Sahaee Hoa Sache Daa Sacha Dhoa, Har, Har, Har: The word *Aap* means Himself, *Sahaee* is protector or rescuer, *Hoa* is "has become." *Sache Daa Sacha* means "the Truest of the True," and *Dhoa* is "has carried." The meaning of the mantra is, "The Lord Himself has become the protector, the Truest of the True has taken care of us, God, God, God."

Ong Kar Nirankar Nirankar Ong: Ong Kar means "God, as He manifests in Creation." *Nirankar* means "God without form." Together, the mantra represents God manifested and formless.

Gobinde, Mukande, Udaare, Apaare, Hariang, Kariang, Nirnaame, Akaame: This is the *Guru Gaitri mantra* for protection. The translation is "Sustainer, Liberator, Enlightener, Infinite, Destroyer, Creator, Nameless, Desireless."

Keep Up! This is the Maha (great) mantra of the Aquarian Age.

Jaap Sahib

Jaap Sahib is a Sikh prayer, or bani, which was written by Guru Gobind Singh, the tenth of the Sikh Gurus. Several of the exercises in this manual were done in rhythm to and while meditatively listening to this prayer set to music. The following are some of Yogi Bhajan's comments on the power of this sound current and the beauty and effects of exercising with it:

This summer I want to show you how in very old times, in a state of ecstasy, people used to worship God through yogic exercise. That is how I learned *Jaap Sahib*, by exercising with it. Do it with devotion. Sing it! Copy it! Become sharp. There is nothing in *Jaap Sahib* you have to learn. It is a naad (sound current). I'm telling you how Guru Gobind Singh uplifted his people who were crippled mentally and physically. A movement started where these people began elevating themselves and becoming conscious and becoming visible to God, and God became visible to man. And victory over oppression came when Guru Gobind Singh used the praise of the Lord in naad. That is what is beautiful about *Jaap Sahib*. It raises the soul and the self of the being. And that is what we are talking about. I'm just trying to give you the experience of how I learned *Gurbani* (the words of the Gurus) and I learned Kundalini Yoga...

If you can learn to pronounce *Jaap Sahib*, God will give you power to speak and listen well. A person who does not know how to listen can never improve himself. And a person who cannot learn to speak, cannot improve anything. Power is the word, how you receive it and how you deliver it. Power is the word.

Always remember the most powerful, effective way is to copy *Jaap Sahib*, because you are not copying the words, you are copying the creative essence of the word, the naad. There is no other way that you can learn about sensitivity. If you can practice on this meditatively, then whatever people will say, you will always compute what they mean. It will give you a totally different dimension. It will take away your unawareness, foolishness, and nonsense. Because whatever people say, you will always compute what they are actually saying. What a person is saying and what he is actually saying are two different dimensions. And that is what I am going to give you the experience of through these exercises.

You have to understand one thing - the Sikhs of Guru Gobind Singh were in a position to run at the speed of galloping horses. Now explain it to me, what miracle was that? *Jaap Sahib*. *Jaap Sahib* gives you the strength of the mind behind every muscle of yours. And if you want to change, you have to take the Name of God everywhere, with every breath. It should be in you and you should recite it, and you should be with it, and you should become it. And that is the way to be spiritual. Everything you do should be right from your spirit, and your spirit should be with it. That's the way you can succeed. Anything else will not work it out. When you do things and the Word of God is with you, when you live like this, then the Word of God on your tongue makes you God.

When Guru Gobind Singh recited *Jaap Sahib*, he knew it already, he didn't have a problem. He did it for all, he gave us *Jaap Sahib*. When your grace, your power, your position is in danger, that is what this bani was given to you for. Whosoever recites this *bani* shall never fall flat on his face. That's why an ordinary bunch of bones could fight with thousands and thousands of trained armed soldiers and defend themselves beautifully, because they had spirit with them. And this is the way to have spirit.

You have a very limited imagination of God. The greatest sin is to imagine God in a limited way. When you imagine the Unlimited in a limited way, it is the greatest insult. And we insult God every day through every action because we have no imagination, or we never make an effort to imagine that God is unlimited. That is the basic problem of our life. The mess we are creating around us is that we feel that God is limited and we can grab It. Therefore we cannot enjoy the unlimited nature of God.

In *Jaap Sahib* they took every aspect of God and bowed and bowed and bowed. That's what Guru Gobind Singh did; he didn't do anything more than that. He brought God and His aspect to the whole thing, *namo, namo, namo, namo.* "You are an idiot, You are most intelligent, You are sickness, You are health." You know what that gives you? That gives you fearlessness, *nirbhao.* When you feel God is everywhere, then you become fearless, and when you become fearless, then you have no vengeance, then you won't make cliques, then you won't play games, and then you won't misuse reason and logic and have arguments and waste your time on nonsense.

Jaap Sahib is the salutation to God in which Guru Gobind Singh recites every facet of God. As many facets as have been explained there, that many facets you have to cover in your life. That's what *Jaap Sahib* is. You have to deal with each facet. If you want to do that, you require about 250 living years for each facet to learn, practice, experience and project. I don't think we have that time. So basically, the idea of the mantra is, it gives you the key to the opening of the plateau, to that hemisphere where you want to be. That's what *Jaap Sahib* does and when you do it with these exercises, it will keep you healthy, happy and holier than you can think. You can enjoy life.

Now, there is another thing in *Jaap Sahib* which you might not have ever understood. If you can mentally remember and verbally recite *Ek Achree Chand*, it doesn't matter what your karmas are, it doesn't matter who you are, if you can remember it and recite it 11 times, there's nothing as a woman you need as a grace which shall not be bestowed upon you by the hand of God. Not by any human being. No human being can give you anything anyway.

Jaap Sahib is not just to praise the God. I have experienced and I believe that these things are there to make us highly sensitive, absolutely creative and extremely intuitive. It doesn't matter how rich you are, how healthy you are, how good you are. It doesn't matter if you have all the faculties of life which you want to have. If you are not intuitive, you are dumb. That's where the buck stops. That is where life is depreciated, that's where pain comes. And that is what I'm trying to take you past. For that you need new blood. That's why we are doing these exercises, so that the glands can work. And for that you also need the knowledge of hydrotherapy, *ishnaan.*

Gurmukhi Vowel Transliteration Key

This key is applicable for all *Gurmukhi* words that have been spelled phonetically in this manual.

Transliteration	Pronounced as in
a	America
aa	father
i	big
ee	feet
u	put
oo	school
e	pray, great
ai	mat
o	hope
au	sounds midway between or and our

Music Used in This Manual

1. *Jaap Sahib,* Ragi Sat Nam Singh
2. *Dukh Bhanjan,* Ragi Sat Nam Singh
3. *Sukhmani Sahib,* Singh Kaur Khalsa
4. *Bara Maha-The Twelve Months,* Don Cooper
5. *Wahe Guru Wahe Jeeo,* Bhai Avtar Singh & Bhai Gurucharan Singh
6. *Aap Sahaee Hoa Sache Da Sacha Dhoa, Har, Har, Har*

The music used in this manual is available from **Ancient Healing Ways,** www.a-healing.com, 800.359.2940.

"Nobility:"

Chorus -
>   Noble is a virtue that affects every soul
>   As innocence affects the heart
>   Woman has one virtue to be noble till death
>   Living nobly is very blessed
>   Living your Truth is happiness

Verse 1
>   Noble is a virtue of the presence of God
>   Greatest virtue that can be expressed
>   Noble through everyone whatever they may be
>   Before the one God equality
>   *(Chorus)*

Verse 2
>   A noble woman gives birth to a noble life
>   Noble children and surroundings be
>   A noble woman looks and lives nobility
>   Even if she lives in poverty
>   *(Chorus)*

Verse 3
>   Unlike a mirror distorted when it is cracked
>   Noble habits are a noble life
>   Don't barter character values for benefits
>   Noble one of God does not forget
>   *(Chorus)*

Verse 4
>   Nobility is manufactured inside
>   Training of exerting self-esteem
>   To see herself confirms a virtuous face
>   Selfless living grace through time and space
>   *(Chorus)*

"Oh That Mean, Mean Man:"
Yogi Bhajan said that if you understand this song, you will give up guilt.

>   Oh that mean, mean man
>   He sins and sins again and again
>   If he chants the name of the Lord
>   Four corners of the world will bow down to him
>   Four corners of the world will bow down.

"The Khalsa Way:"
Yogi Bhajan said that the family which regularly sings this song will have no troubles.

Long ago and far away a man sat like a stone
On a burning seat of red hot coals, to him it was a throne
For he was Guru Arjan Dev king of this world and the next
When he finished his time in this earthly world
He just smiled and left.
As it was in the beginning and shall be for all time
Those who live and die a fearless life in the court of God they shine.

Chorus)
That is the Khalsa way, I don't mind dying and I won't go crying
That is the Khalsa way, if things look bad we just keep on trying
That is the Khalsa way, if anyone falls, ten more will come in his place
That is our way.

The Mogul king sent forth his word; no Sikh shall be left alive
We'll wipe the Khalsa from the face of the earth,
On each head he put a price
So one brave Sikh stood in the road, knowing he couldn't live long
In the name of the Guru he collected a toll; He shook that king to his throne
They tried to put the light of the Khalsa out,
And now it is they who are gone
Through every test of time and space Khalsa lives on

(Chorus)
One by one they shot us down as we read from the Siri Guru
`Till they had to stop, they'd never seen so many who'd die for the truth
And those who laid on the railroad tracks
Their bodies stopped the trains
Those whose children were killed before their eyes
They saw God through their pain
And all those who stood their ground against impossible odds
In their fearlessness and courage
We see the power of God

(Chorus)
Twenty million started out, only a few survive
But we stood together in the heart of this land
Against all their power and lies
They wish that we'd never been, they clubbed us in the streets
But our hearts were strong
The war was won,
Our victory was peace
They waited for us all to disappear
They waited for our spirit to die
But they'll still be waiting when the sun burns out
For heroes and warriors,
The saints and the martyrs
Will never die.
(Chorus)

"All Things Come From God:"
This song is available on a recording entitled *"Anahata"*

Chorus:
One thing to remember is
All things come from God and all things go to God
All things come from God and all things go to God
Everything comes from Him and it goes back home again
All things come from God and all things go to God
All things come from God and all things go to God

Verse:
No power to speak or silence to keep
No power to beg, no power to give,
No power to die, no power to live.

(Chorus)

Verse:
No power to rule, or enlighten the mind.
No power to awaken my soul to Thee
No power to find the way to be free.
By his own will, Oh Nanak, none can be good or bad.
He alone has the power to reveal the way.